The KENT Weather Book

Floods and freezes, tempests and tornadoes, deluges and dust-devils, hailstones and heatwaves — from day to day the weather pattern changes. We are told that global warming may be the cause of recent extremes but in the hop-gardens and orchards, on the chalk cliffs and downs and across the rich marshland of Kent, the climate has always been immensely variable. Yes, the train that should have arrived on platform two really was stranded in a snowdrift. Yes, grandad was telling the truth when he said he paddled down the High Street in a canoe. Yes, Canterbury did hold the record for the hottest day ever known. And here is the proof. A unique pictorial record of Kent's most dramatic weather events.

Bob Ogley, Ian Currie and Mark Davison

Froglets Publications Ltd

Brasted Chart,
Westerham,
Kent TN16 1LY

Tel: 01959 562972
Fax: 01959 565365

ISBN 9781872337951

First printed October 1991 Reprinted November 1991,
August 1993, September 1997, November 2000, October
2007

Front cover illustration
Bus in the Snow, Pratts Bottom 1952
John Topham, Top Foto

Back cover illustrations
Storm tossed, 16.10.1987
Knole Park, Sevenoaks
Les Hunt

This book was scanned, printed and bound by
Thanet Press, Union Crescent, Margate,
CT9 1NU.

Artwork by *Alison Clarke*

Acknowledgements

THIS book has been written because there are many people in Kent who want to know more about the history of the weather in their county, to wonder at its amazing variety and to study photographs of the more memorable events. It is one of a series of county books on the history of the weather. The other in print titles can be found on page 184.

We would like to thank the staff of libraries and museums who have provided considerable help in our research, editors and photographers of local newspapers and local history enthusiasts who have given valued advice and, in many cases, provided a "missing" photograph. We are indebted also to members of the public who have responded to our appeal in newspapers. Many forgotten historic moments have come to light in dusty Kentish attics and cellars.

We are particularly indebted to the Climatological Observers' Link, Royal Meteorological Society, Journal of Meteorology, British Rainfall Network, the Environment Agency and The Kent Messenger

Many of the photographs are provided by Topfoto, one of the largest picture libraries in the world. John Topham started his picture agency before the second world war and worked in harness with national and local newspapers. With his sharp eye for detail, his obvious nose for news and his ability to get to the scene before his opponents, John Topham became a legend in this field. Alan Smith has developed the library to its current prestigious position.

Photographs

Photographs in this book are the copyright of the following: Topfoto 9, 41 (bottom), 43, 45, 48 49, 50, 52, 56, 58, 61, 62, 63, 64, 65, 66, 69, 73, 79 (top), 80, 82, 84 (bottom), 86 (top), 90, 92, 96, 97, 98 (bottom), 100, 102 (top) and bottom), 103, 108, 117, 133. Kent Messenger 38 (bottom), 46, 54, 59 (top), 70, 71 (bottom), 74, 76, 81, 84 (top), 89, 107, 110, 111, 113, 114, 118, 120, 122 (top), 127, 128, 131 (bottom), 139, 140 (top), 141, 148 (top), 166, 167 168,169,170/1,173. Kent County Library Service 10, 13, 19, 20, 26 (top), 27, 28, 29, 30, 32, 33, 35, 42. Kentish Times 55, 67, 71 (Top), 79 (bottom), 85, 87, 95, 112, 116. Chris Fright 22, 59 (bottom), 72, 88, 119. Peter Bamford 12, 14, 21, 44. Jerry Banchet 26 (bottom), 31. Bromley Borough Library 15, 23, 38 (top), Bexley Borough Library 60, 93, 98 (top right). Bob Hollingsbee 16, 86(bottom). Kent Fire Brigade 98 (top left), 148 (bottom). National River Authority (Environment Agency) 101, Southern Water 178 (bottom). Sheerness Times 78. Chatham News 124, 132, 154. Surrey Mirror 125. East Kent Mercury 129, 130, 131(top). Folkestone Herald (AKN/Trinity Mirror) 136, 144, 160, 161, 181. Gravesend Reporter 177, Kentish Express 140 (bottom). Heather Crease 25. Charles Wanostrocht 106, 122 (bottom). D.Weaver Countrywide Photographic 99. Mark Davison: 137. Kevin Harvey 153. Roger Johnson 150. Fern Ogley 155, 157, 176 (bottom), 179. Dover Express (AKN) 158. Roy Letkey 157. Phyllida Warner 162. Holly Pelling 152, Jerome Bennett 159, Paul Amos/The Environment Agency 164. Ian Currie 163,178. John King 176.Meridian TV 180 (bottom). D. Benjeyfield 175. Other sources Kent and Sussex Courier, Alex Watson, Bob Ogley.

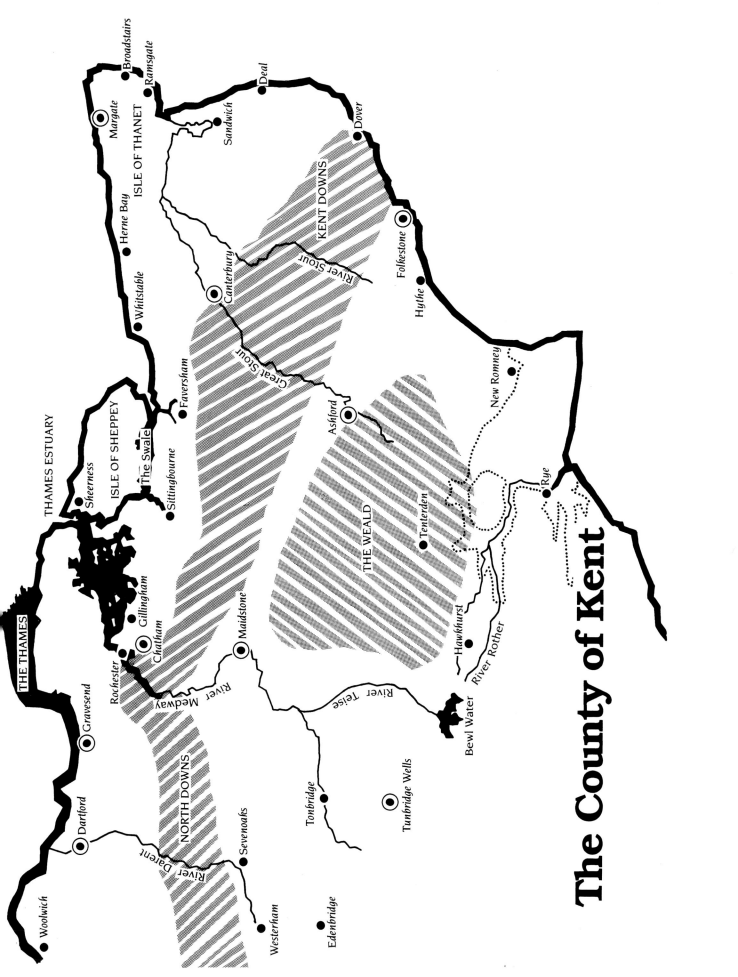

The County of Kent

At War with the Wind and Waves

THOUSANDS of years ago, near the end of the fourth Ice Age, Kent was part of the Continent of Europe and the River Thames was a tributary of The Rhine. The waves, aided and abetted by the weather have changed all that. Breaking through about 6,000 years ago, the sea, whipped up by constant gales, has since reconstructed the coast of Kent. Today, we find the mediaeval port of Sandwich two and a half miles inland and the subsidiary Cinque Port of Tenterden a countryside market town. Much of Romney Marsh has been reclaimed from the sea but most of Reculver is still submerged beneath the waves.

The county we know as the "Garden of England" stands in a unique climatic position, the closest to the bitter winds that blast from the Russian steppes yet the nearest to the shimmering heat that often lies over the continent in summer - a heat that breeds some of our most severe storms.

Kent has experienced a long and remarkable association with the wind and the waves. From the Great Flood Barrier at Woolwich and the low-lying towns of the Thames Estuary, past the industrial Medway connurbations, the Saxon shore of Sheppey and the bucket and spade resorts of Thanet, to the Channel ports and the marshland of Romney, the coastline stretches for 126 miles. Every single town, village and hamlet has been at war with the weather and these pages reflect a few battles won and many more lost.

To the people of Kent, like those of other counties, the weather is a perpetual topic of conversation. The climate is temperate and mostly benign. Suddenly, however, it can change as is proved by the storm-ridden tidal surge which overtopped the defences in every north-Kent coastal town on the last day of January, 1953 and flooded thousands of homes.

Inland, the county experiences a whole range of extreme conditions. The marshy lands of north Kent slope up to the North Downs, which enter Kent from Surrey to the north of Westerham and like a great backbone stretch down to the Shakespeare Cliff at Dover. The Downs east of Maidstone are notorious for their heavy snow in late winter and early spring. Many older people will recall the blizzards of 1927 and 1947 which produced, in places, some three feet of undrifted snow. The Downs and the Greensand Ridge to the south also take the full impact of the more furious winds. The Great Storm, or so-called "hurricane" of 1987 rendered enormous damage, tearing up millions of trees in the county, particularly on the hillsides. There had been nothing like it since the storm of 1703 when Daniel Defoe counted 17,000 uprooted trees in Kent before he gave up his self-imposed task.

In the valleys of Kent between the chalk flint and ragstone hills run the rivers, dominated by the Medway, which actually rises in the High Weald of Sussex and meanders through orchards and hopfields before carving its way north to meet the Thames. The Medway is 70 miles in length and is fed by many tributaries - the Eden, Shode, Teise, Beult, Loose and Len. There is also a little sister, the Darent, and to the east and south, the Great and Lesser Stour and the mysterious Rother. To the north-east is the Swale.

In days of great gales or deluges, and there have been many, the rivers of Kent have burst their banks and flooded the land. They have flooded towns too. In Maidstone and Tonbridge on the Medway, Edenbridge on the Eden, Sandwich, Ashford and Canterbury on the Stour, Cranbrook on the Crane, Faversham and Sittingbourne on the Swale, Westerham and Dartford on the Darent, wild waves have lapped down High Streets, through shops and homes bringing with them all the usual heartbreak and chaos. Looking through the county newspapers from the mid-nineteenth century each great flood was the "worst in living memory". It depends how old you are but what event was more disastrous than that brought about by the torrential rainfall of September 1968?

In Kent there have been such phenomena as whirlwinds, dust-devils, tornadoes and even earthquakes. An earthquake destroyed the Bell Tower at Canterbury and fork lightning has struck church towers in all corners of Kent. On one memorable occasion hailstones pelted down so furiously in a summer storm that the town of Tunbridge Wells was several feet deep in ice. Amazingly, the same town suffered in a repeat performance 34 years later.

Many people of Kent have lost their lives in blizzards, storms and floods but the greatest mass killer was the smog of 1952 which choked hundreds of commuters and those living in Kent's north-east surburban towns. At the other extreme are the long, hot summers of 1975/6 and 1989/90 when temperatures soared to the nineties, a thousand fires developed, rivers and reservoirs ran dry, garden hoses were banned and people decided to give the Med a miss and head for Thanet and the Forelands.

It is ironic that Kent, with its long railway tunnel under the sea and the breaking up of Continental barriers, should be almost part of Normandy once more. Whether you are a Man of Kent or a Kentish Man you will agree that those with the greatest influence on our way of life have been the warriors — the Saxons, the Romans, the Normans and the Weather.

In the case of the latter, the battle goes on.

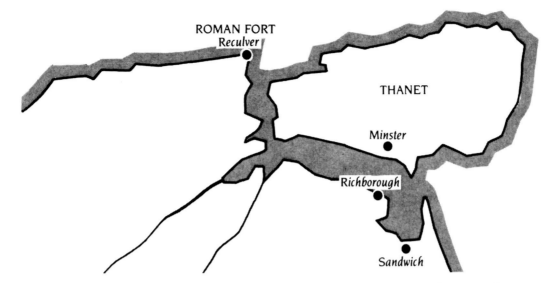

When Thanet Really was an Island

A stranger driving towards the Isle of Thanet could be forgiven for wondering why it is called an island. After all, the Rivers Wantsum and Stour which separate Thanet from the mainland are mere trickles and the surrounding rich, flat, fertile marshland looks as if it has been there for centuries.

Not so. As recently as the reign of Henry VIII, the Isle of Thanet was separated from mainland Kent by a stretch of water known as the Wantsum Channel. It cut through from Richborough and Sandwich to Reculver, which was also at the mouth of an open bay. Ships from Boulogne and Calais sailing to London went through the Wantsum rather than going round the dangerous North Foreland. In earlier days a sizeable creek ran close to Minster Church and the channel was navigable by merchant ships.

In Roman times the Wantsum Channel was more than a mile wide in places but a series of severe storms rendered it unnavigable and it silted up and slowly shrank to its present size.

Caesar's Fleet Swept Back to Gaulle

Summer of 55 BC

WEATHER forecasting has progressed enormously in the twentieth century. Without such knowledge even the greatest among us are but putty in the hands of the elements.

Julius Caesar must have been one of the earliest to realise this when his expeditionary force arrived in Britain in the late summer of 55 BC. He was thought to have landed between Walmer and Deal and eagerly awaited his cavalry transport ships, an integral part of his military strategy. However, an intense storm brought gales, and a storm surge to the eastern Channel swept them back to France and dashed to pieces some of his beached ships. Others were rendered useless. This left him with the daunting prospect of surviving in a hostile land without cavalry, corn, ships and supplies. He therefore spent time repairing his fleet and departed, though not before repelling successfully an attack on his camp.

The following year Caesar returned and brought 35,000 men and 4,000 cavalry to the shores of Kent.

On the outward journey they had to endure a calm and were pulled off course by the tide. In spite of having detailed plans of engagement he had apparently learnt little about Kentish weather from the previous year and made the same mistake of incorrectly beaching his ships on arrival. Again a storm brought high winds which smashed 40 ships and crippled the rest, amounting to some 700 vessels.

Time was wasted in effecting repairs but nonetheless he still marched his troops through Kent via Canterbury, forded the Thames and defeated Cassivellaunus, the leader of the Britons, near St Albans.

However, the weather continued to plague him and strong north winds prevented 60 newly constructed ships built in France from reaching Kent. This made it necessary for Caesar to cram all his troops into available boats and head across the Channel. The wind dropped and they had to row back to Gaul, aided by the tide, to ponder the vicissitudes of Albion's weather.

Rother Blown Off Course

ROMNEY Marsh, in the time of the Roman occupation, was a great bay surrounded by sandstone cliffs with long creeks running inland. Oxney, Winchelsea, Lydd, Romney and Rye were islands; the sea reached right into the creeks of the Rivers Rother, Tillingham and Brede and lapped against the cliffs of Playden, Peasmarsh and Tenterden. The Rother — the largest river — had two courses. One meandered from Appledore and into the bay near Romney. The other cut a channel to the sea at Hythe.

Over the years nature had played many games with Romney Marsh. The ups and downs in the tidal movements had created a series of depressions. On several occasions the land was submerged and then re-appeared above sea-level. The most momentous event, perhaps in the whole geographical history of Kent, came in the last half of the thirteenth century with two terrific tempests. The first, in 1250, was described by the Kentish scribe, Holinshed: "On the first day of October, 1250, the moon, upon her change appearing red and swelled began to show tokens of the great tempest of wind that followed, which was so huge and mightie, both by land and sea, that the like had not been lightlie knowne, and seldome, or rather never, heard of by men then alive. The sea, forced contrarie to his natural course flowed twice without ebbing, yielding such a rooring that the same was heard (not without great wonder) a far distance from the shore. Moreover the same sea appeared in the dark of the night to burne as it had been on fire, and the waves to strive and fight together after a marvellous sort, so that the mariners could not devise how to save their ships. At Hert-burne three tall ships perished without recoverie, besides other smaller vessels. At Winchelsey, besides other hurt that was done, in bridges, milles, breakes and banks, there were three hundred houses and some churches drowned with the high rising of the water course."

In 1287 the "tempest of all tempests" roared up the Channel. What remained of Old Winchelsea was utterly destroyed. In fact the island and its beaches were swept away leaving no trace. Today the area is dry land again but no-one can point with any exactness to the site of what was Old Winchelsea

In his history of Romney Marsh, Walter J. Murray writes that no West Indian hurricane more completely wiped out a town than did this storm. The size and weight of the waves smashed the badly damaged sea walls, swept away wooden buildings like so much matchwood and scoured away the foundations of sand and shingle on which the town was built. Miraculously it was not inhabited. King Edward I had already decided that Winchelsea must be evacuated and re-established. He sited that new town on the hill at the eastern end of the Brede Creek a little south-west of Rye.

"One wonders", writes Mr Murray, "how those Barons and the multitude of Winchelsea felt during those terrible hours as the gigantic waves stormed across the bay and thundered against the cliffs of their new stronghold. One pictures them crouched against the brow of the hill peering through the blinding spray and under the lash of a hurricane. It must have seemed like the end of the world".

To the people of Romney it almost was. As they dragged themselves from their drowned houses and looked around at the appalling havoc they saw, to their horror, that the Rother had changed its course. The river which flowed into the great bay was choked with shingle, sand and debris but that was not all. Hythe Haven was nearly closed, Romney Marsh was badly flooded, Bromehill, a little town to the west, between Lydd and Old Winchelsea, had just disappeared. Lydd was still there but its buttresses of shingle were more vast than ever. All around was the wreckage of ships, inns, houses and churches. The bodies of men were strewn around the shore for many miles.

Where was the River Rother? It had straightened its course and was flowing almost directly from Appledore to Rye, where the Tillingham and Brede also reached the sea. In triple measure Rye was to benefit and Romney, without its port, was to suffer.

The people of Romney attempted to bring the river back by digging out the old course along the Rhee Wall from Appledore. But they failed to coax the Rother back. The new cut rapidly silted up. So did the great bay of Romney. Ships which had tied up to the walls of the church could no longer approach. Romney, a Cinque Port, became an inland town.

The Cinque Port of Hythe suffered a similar fate. So did Tenterden, a subsidiary Cinque Port. The only ancient towns to maintain their seafaring estate were Rye and New Winchelsea which now prospered. But the storms were still raging and the sea was still winning. Over the centuries, Walland and Guldeford Marshes were "inned" and the Brede was silted up. Winchelsea was left stranded and only Rye remained. Then, in 1572, there was another storm. This one drove so violently inland that the sea broke into the low-lying land behind the town and the harbour was enlarged.

Great storms have helped to change the map of England. Towns have disappeared and others have been created. Some hundred square miles of the richest agricultural land in Britain have been added to the county of Kent. A Kentish river now flows into Sussex. The story of Romney Marsh is one of the most absorbing in the history of England.

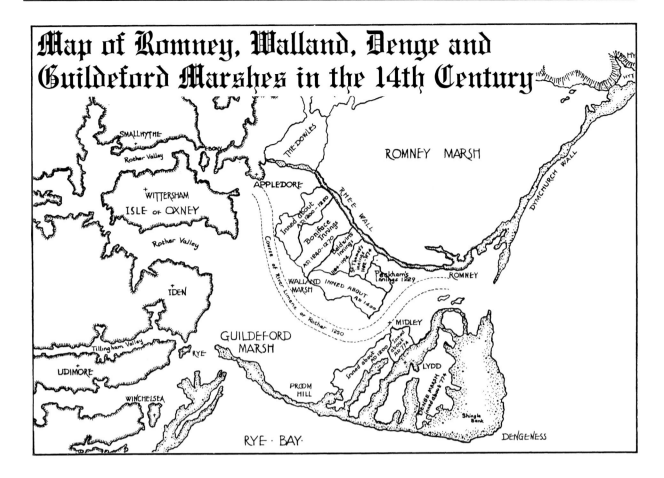

Map of Romney, Walland, Denge and Guildeford Marshes in the 14th Century

The Weather in the Early Years

1236: The chronicler, Holinshed, described how a great tide pounded at the east "for several days with unbated fury, washing up the Ocean in such tremendous waves that the banks gave way and the whole country lay completely exposed to its awful fury". The toll of human life was appalling. According to Holinshed "in one village there were buried one hundred corpses".

1624: On 3rd-4th October 120 vessels at anchor in the Goodwin Sands were wrecked. Twenty completely disappeared in "a terrible gale — the like of which hazs never been seen".

1672: On 29th December at 11pm in "Bennenden a pretty considerable town in the Wild of Kent, appeared a very great light. This lightning was seconded by hideous and distracted thunder which occasioned many inhabitants to hide themselves fearing the houses should drop in a heap of flame and ruins". The anger of God was feared and confirmed when the church was struck. "The devouring flames and impetuous thunder found no great resistance from this stony pile. The steeple was quickly forced to resign itself to that earth it was first fixed; so that the fabrick and frame began to incorporate with its own foundations."

1684: Persistent northerly winds in the coldest recorded winter swept polar ice south from the Arctic and through the Dover Straits, closing the sea ports for some days.

1743: "A fearful gale in East Kent." On 23rd-24th February twelve ships were lost, 52 men drowned. Many vessels were driven ashore between Sandwich and Walmer.

1776: A great storm of thunder and lightning was followed by a sudden inundation of flood water which overflowed into the greater part of the City of Canterbury. Several people were drowned.

1807: The entire coastline between North and South Foreland was strewn with wreckage as a severe gale hit Kent on 18th February. Thirty six vessels were wrecked. There was heavy loss of life and property on land

EARTHQUAKES IN KENT

The Sea Foamed and Ships Tottered

21st May, 1382

WILLIAM Courtenay, Archbishop of Canterbury was presiding over a synod to condemn the doctrines of John Wycliffe in Blackfriars on 21st May, 1382 when a great rumble from deep in the earth violently shook the building. Pandemonium spread throughout London and the Archbishop's meeting ended abruptly, both sides claiming that God had intervened on their behalf.

The bell tower of Canterbury Cathedral was severely damaged and the six bells "shook down". Cloister walls from the Chapter House to the Dormitory were ruined. Substantial harm was reported at St. Augustine's Abbey in Canterbury. West of Canterbury, All Saints Church at Hollingbourne sustained "grave ruin" to the chancel.

This was the first earthquake to stand out as a significant event in contemporary history which describes the Archbishop's meeting at Blackfriars as "Council of the Earthquake".

6th April, 1580

St Peter's Church, Broadstairs was cracked from top to bottom by an earthquake when "the sea foamed and ships tottered. There was heard from the southwest a marvellouse great noyse, as in the twingling of an eye the same noyse was as though yt had been round about the hearers; and therwith began a most feirce and terrible earthquake".

The churches of St. Peter's and St. Mary's at Sandwich were damaged and Saltwood Castle was "ruinous". Dover Castle lost part of its wall when some of the cliff collapsed. Portions of St. Nicholas Church, Plumstead were shaken down. In London Thomas Gray and Mabel Everite, who were struck and killed by stones falling from Christ Church, Newgate, became the first identified victims of a British earthquake.

8th September, 1692

A history of Deal reports that houses were shaken, chimneys fell, kitchen utensils were thrown from the shelves and beds shook under their occupants. Several houses and the Norman castle in Tonbridge were damaged. Leeds Castle, near Maidstone, shook so violently that all in the Castle, including the Lady herself, "went out of it and expected it to fall".

22nd April, 1884

A large earthquake tremor in Essex was also felt at 9.20am on the North Kent coast between Woolwich and Margate. At Strood, "the Board School oscillated so that the master ordered it to be evacuated". The general belief was that an enormous explosion had taken place at the Government Magazines nearby. At Westgate-on-Sea it caused the church bells to ring.

After the 1884 earthquake there was speculation about the boiling water which existed a mile and a half beneath Woolwich and the possibility that the Kent Water Works could, in the future, "tap" the earth and utilise the internal heat to provide instant hot water for homes and factories.

Other earthquakes in Kent include a series of seven between 1089 and 1247.

The Weather in the Early Years

1825: On 2nd November a destructive high tide was whipped up by hurricane force winds. The 513 ton Ogle Castle was lost on Goodwin Sands. More than 100 sailors and passengers died as the ship was entirely engulfed by sand.

1847: Inhabitants of Tunbridge Wells awoke on 4th December to find what appeared to be a mountain river running down the High Street and Mount Pleasant, following an overnight hailstorm. The water filled the cellars of the Castle Inn and many homes and shops were flooded.

New Year's Day, 1861: Hamburg brig Gottenburg, 170 tons driven ashore in thick fog accompanied by snow and hurricane force wind. Distress signals unnoticed. Twenty three killed, including six women.

1867: An unofficial report of the temperature falling as low as -10F (-23C) at East Peckham between 3rd and 5th January.

November 25, 1877: IN a series of great tidal waves which struck the Thanet coast like the blows of a battering ram, 20 vessels were driven ashore on rocks between Westgate and Westbrook. They included 10 schooners, four brigantines, two barques, two luggers, a ketch and a smack. Four lifeboats were launched and the crew of all ships rescued. The only casualty was a sailor with a broken leg.

The Goodwin Sands, from time immemorial, have been associated with peril and destruction but on a beautiful August evening in 1854, they became the venue for an exhilarating game of cricket between the Gentlemen of Walmer and the crew of the Sparten, one of the finest luggers on Deal beach. The Illustrated London News described the occasion in its issue of August 26, 1854. "A sad association of ideas crowded the minds of the cricketers when they arrived on this awfully melancholy place. Here thousands of gallant fellows have been entombed. Here millions of property have been engulfed. And here was a picture contrasting vividly with the present scene of peacetime. The party returned home about ten at night. The evening was fine and the ripples on the surface of the sea, as the lugger ploughed homeward, were most beautifully illuminated with phosphorescent light".

Goodwin — Great Ship Swallower

MORE than 120 ships anchored in The Downs, a four-mile wide channel between the notorious Goodwin Sands and Deal, were badly damaged in a "fearful" storm which swept down the English Channel during 3rd and 4th October, 1624. Many vessels were totally wrecked and 20 vanished, never to be seen again.

Also at anchor in the Downs were two Dunkirk men-o'-war under guard. During the height of the storm, described at the time as "most terrible, the like of which has never been seen", one man-o'-war attempted to escape and was engaged by the flagship of the Dutch Vice-Admiral, Moy Lambert. The Dunkirker blew up and sank with 200 of her crew. In the exchange of fire the Dutch ship also sank

When the great gale abated the Downs were strewn with ground tackle, cannon and the wrecks of many ships. Some were floating, some were partially submerged and some had been swallowed by the sand.

This was not an isolated incident. The Goodwin Sands have been the setting for shipwrecks dating back to the time when men first ventured to sea. Four miles offshore from Deal this series of sandbanks has a reputation among seafarers unrivalled anywhere in the world.

Since the middle ages thousands of vessels have been lost and many have gone unnoticed, for the sands have the capacity to claim ships, break them up and swallow them without trace. Little wonder that Trinity House finds it necessary today to mark the outline of the Goodwins with three lightships and 15 buoys.

This small area of the Kentish coast, nicknamed "Calamity Corner" has a lifeboat history unique in the British Isles. In the 20 miles between Ramsgate, Deal, Walmer and Kingsdown, lifeboats put to sea in the most appalling weather saving, over the years, thousands of lives and providing some of the most heroic and spectacular rescues on record. Many brave lifeboatmen have themselves become victims of the gales.

Authoritative estimates of ships lost in stormy weather on the Goodwin Sands vary between 1,400 and 5,000. Should siltation one day merge the sands with the mainland it may be possible to excavate the area, providing archaeologists with one of the most exciting projects the world has ever known. And it will all be credited to the great gales around Kent's "Calamity Corner".

The twin towers of Reculver, a landmark for navigators.

'Towne' that Disappeared

MALEVOLENT seas, kindled by unrelenting north-easterly gales, have battered the North Kent coast for centuries. Cliffs have been pushed further and further inland, headlands have slipped into the sea and the little Roman town of Reculver has disappeared.

Some years after Julius Ceasar's reconnaisance expeditions landed at Deal, Kent became a frontier settlement for the Romans who enjoyed new-found agricultural prosperity. On the coast the legions built ports and fortresses, Regulbium was among the first. It guarded the northern entrance to the Wantsum Channel.

Two thousand years ago the sea was three quarters of a mile from the fort, and the town, because of its royal associations and presence of an Abbot, enjoyed much importance. Even in mediaeval times it remained the ecclesiastical centre of a vast area. What a harrowing experience it must have been for the inhabitants as they saw the sea eating away so relentlessly at their land and inevitably their houses.

Historian John Leland, in 1540, wrote that the fort stood "withyn a quarter of a myle, or little more, of the sesyde and the towne (of Reculver) is but village lyke". The church stood within the fort area. By 1781 a subsidence of the cliffs had brought down the north wall and this signalled the beginning of the end of Leland's little "village lyke towne".

The vicar called a parish meeting and the exodus began. There were more vicious gales and on 13th October, 1802 the chapel house fell down and, according to parish records, "people came from all parts to see the ruins of village and church". "In 1807 the village became total rack to the mercy of the sea".

Tragedy in the Snow

A ferocious, easterly gale and driving snow raged throughout Christmas Day 1836. There was scarcely any feature that could be recognised in the swirling thickness of icy flakes.

Near Herne Bay that night a young woman, Sarah Port, aged 20, and her brother were returning homeward from Broomfield. Walking just a few yards apart the man turned round to face his sister, having only spoken to her seconds beforehand. She had vanished.

The next morning her body was discovered by her father three quarters of a mile distant. It appeared that the snowstorm was so severe she had missed the track and stumbled into the fields. Unable to hear her brother's cries of anguish she perished through cold and fatigue as she wandered lost in the blizzard.

Storm Claimed Lives of 8,000 People

26th November, 1703

AFTER days of windy, often stormy weather a dreadful tempest struck southern England in the middle of a dark November night and wrought havoc from Cornwall to Kent. The wind blew with such violence as to destroy over 1100 dwelling houses, outhouses and barns in Kent alone and claimed the lives of 8,000 people throughout the country and around our shores.

Brenchley Church near Tonbridge lost its steeple and, lying prone on the ground, it provided many villagers the chance to boast in later life that he or she had leapt over the spire. Scarcely a house was undamaged in Tonbridge and Penshurst Park lost 500 trees. So hard did the wind blow it brought salt laden air in from the Channel and cattle refused to eat the brine- encrusted grass at Cranbrook, 17 miles inland.

The writer Daniel Defoe, who was living in London at the time, captured the horror of the storm in a documentary account published in 1704. It had the graphic title, "The Storm or a Collection of the Most Remarkable casualties and Disasters which happened in the late Dreadful Tempest both by Land and Sea". He counted 17,000 trees down in Kent but quickly gave up the task due to the immense devastation. The storm inspired Defoe to write the book Robinson Crusoe.

A storm which had the power to lift a ship at Whitstable bodily hundreds of yards inland became a maelstrom at sea and nowhere more so than in the "Downs", where there were more than 100 merchant ships and a number of naval vessels at anchor. By dawn many of them had broken to pieces with the loss of over 1,500 lives. Of the night Defoe wrote "no pen could describe it, nor tongue express it, nor thought conceive it unless by one in the extremity of it".

Britain's Hottest Day — or was it?

22nd July, 1868

DR George Hunsley Fielding of Grove House, Mill Lane, Tonbridge was a meteorologist who faithfully submitted his readings to the Royal Observatory each week. When he stepped into his garden on the sweltering hot evening of 22nd July, 1868 to check his weather intruments he was amazed. The shade temperature was 100.5F (38.1C) — a reading that was to secure for Tonbridge a place in history books.

The good doctor looked again at his instrument and found he had made no mistake. In fact the temperature in the sun was 142F — a reading which provided a fitting climax to a most extraordinary year.

Day after day the sun bore down from a cloudless sky on to a parched earth. Tonbridge, like every town in Kent, wilted in the heat through May, June and July — and every day seemed hotter. Food had to be thrown away, people walked on the shady side of the street, cattle died for want of water and flies pestered everyone. In this highly fashionable mid- Victorian age when modesty was the vogue and layers of clothing were worn, people struggled to keep cool.

In his report to the Meteorogical Society, Dr Fielding wrote: "The summer may fairly be said to have embraced five months, from May to September inclusive; and the intense heat, combined with the scarcity of rain, was most fatal in its effects upon the animal and vegetable world. The Registrar-General's returns for the quarter ending September 30th showed a fearful increase in England alone, of 21,000 deaths.

"The suffocating heat of July 21st and 22nd I shall never forget; the sky was cloudless with scarcely a breath of air, and what there was felt more as if it had passed through an oven."

Dr Fielding said: "I think it as well to prevent cavilling by stating that I hope I may be trusted as I was for a long time one of Mr Glaisher's staff of observers." (James Glaisher FRS was superintendent of the Royal Observatory's magnetic and meteorological department.) "I have to be on solid ground as I find my brother meteorologists are a "genus irritabile" greatly endowed with the "disputandi pruius".

The reading on that July day in 1868 found its way into the Guinness Book of Records and for a long time was regarded as Britain's hottest day but the remarkable reading of 100.5F (38.1C) was read in a stand, open at the front and probably gave a figure that was too high. In order to achieve standardisation all measurements now are made in a Stevenson Screen designed by Thomas. father of the famous writer and poet Robert Louis. It consists of a white box with louvred sides and insulated roof. It is often mistaken for a bee-hive.

The official record is 99F (37.1C) observed at Cheltenham on 3rd August, 1990. Previously Canterbury's with 98F (36.7C) on 9th August, 1911 held the official record for 79 years.

One man was killed and many people rescued by boats when the sea surged through Hythe on New Year's Day, 1877.

Unhappy New Year for Hythe

IT was New Year's Day, 1877. Workmen at Hythe had been digging out shingle from the banked-up beach for the construction of a sea wall along the front at Stade Street, when a south-westerly blew in. The sea, enlarged by a spring high tide, found the cut made by the builder's men, breached the landward side and rushed towards the town centre. Within minutes water had flowed over the raised banks and bridges of the Hythe Canal and into the cellars of the High Street which itself was awash. One man, a road foreman, was drowned. Others were rescued from the High Street and Marine Walk by boats.

With such a dramatic start 1877 continued to be a memorable year. Throughout the autumn, gales were persistent and severe but on the night of 11th November the wind howled with hurricane force and at first light six ships were seen to be stranded in Pegwell Bay. Others were protruding just above the surface at Gull Stream, a mile north-east of Ramsgate. That night the crews of the Ramsgate and Deal Lifeboats rescued scores of men from the stricken vessels, winning admiration from many quarters and special citations for bravery.

On 24th November they were in action again in a terrible storm. During the night a schooner bound from South Shields to Devon with coal, plunged straight into Deal pier, rebounded, then struck a second time, smashing four of the cast-iron pillars and ripping up the wooden deck. Somehow the toll keeper managed to pull the mate, James Callard, and a 14-year-old boy to safety before the vessel went right under the pier and out the other side. The wreck then struck the sea wall near the Time Ball Tower, capsized and broke into pieces, drowning Captain Head and two seamen. Almost 200 feet of the pier had been demolished and the refreshment room destroyed.

The following day 20 vessels were driven ashore on rocks between Westgate and Westbrook. They included 10 schooners, four brigatines, two barques, two luggers, a ketch and a smack. Again the lifeboats were launched including the two from Margate, Quiver and her larger companion, Friends of All Nations. They rescued 130 people.

Keble's Gazette described the scene in Margate: "Inhabitants on Sunday morning witnessed a scene of devastation and ruin so complete that the only parallel was in a nightmare. In the High Street the ketch Anne had made an unsuccessful attempt to get into the Misses Woodcock's verandah and the Robert and Hannah had essayed to mount The Terrace, keeping close company with the lugger Industry."

The final toll in this tragic year was 47 ships ashore

The first sad chapter in the battered and bruised history of Margate Pier was written on New Year's Day, 1877 when a storm-driven wreck sliced through the pier and marooned 40 to 50 people at the seaward end. They were not rescued until the following day. The jetty and droit office suffered costly damage at the hands of the spring tide. Twenty years later, in December 1897, there was a further assault on the pier by a tidal surge. The pier, built in 1853, somehow managed to survive for 125 years .. until the superstructure collapsed during the storm of 1978.

19th Century Weather Notes

1879: The densest fog of the winter visited London and north Kent on 22nd December and quickly enveloped the day into misty obscurity. Advantage of the conditions was taken by many for felonious purposes.

1886: In February, frozen ponds and lakes in many parts of west Kent became skating rinks as temperatures remained well below freezing. The Sevenoaks Chronicle reported: "It is amusing to watch the tactics of the Sabbath breakers. Men and boys of the labouring classes carry their skates boldly while others hide their skates in bags."

1890-1892: Three successive years of severe weather brought enormous quantities of snow to many parts of Kent. In November 1890 the snow in Maidstone reached a depth of 22 inches and December was the coldest on record. On the 30th Cranbrook did not exceed 22F (-6C). In March 1891 a great snowstorm swept through the county. It was finely grained and

was driven into every nook and cranny by storm force winds. In Sevenoaks a young boy was prosecuted for throwing a snowball at Mr Tommy Skinner, a local councillor. On 15th and 16th April 1892 snow was a foot deep on the level at Hoo and driven into deep drifts by a gale from the north.

1893: The Great Spring Drought: An absolute drought occurred at Maidstone. Mount House reported 60 days in a row without any measurable rain.

1897: February was wet and dull and influenza was rife at Sevenoaks. It was mild in December, too, and primroses, roses and polyanthus were in flower at Sevenoaks on Christmas Day.

1899: The dry weather continued and at Sheldwich a well, some 170 feet deep and holding 12 feet of water earlier in the decade, was by the end of this year only two feet six inches deep in water.

Two men were killed and many injured during a landslip at Folkestone Warren on 12th January, 1877 a few days after the big storm. The slip was about 100 acres in extent and took place at the eastern end of the Martello Tunnel, blocking the main line completely with chalk and rubble to a depth of more than 30 feet. On 17th March, 1877 a single line working was restored.

The Walmer Lifeboat was called into service on 25th November, 1877 when a great tidal wave struck the Kent coast. Four lifeboats were launched on that day to rescue the crews of schooners, brigs, barques, luggers and smacks — and all were brought safely ashore. This painting by Thomas Rose Miles shows the scene on Walmer beach as the intrepid lifeboatmen prepared for another mission. Their families were there, to wish them good luck.

The Walmer Tornado

24th October, 1878

THE sentry on duty at the Jubilee Gate entrance to the Royal Marine Barracks at Walmer showed little concern for the moderate souwester which was blowing. So far the autumn of 1878 had been tranquil, October was still clinging to summer and by the 24th the leaves were just beginning to turn.

The young marine's thoughts were rudely interrupted as the wind shifted to the south, a full gale developed and the sentry box rattled violently. Suddenly it crashed to the ground trapping him inside. He struggled to free himself and became a bruised witness to a tornado which tore through Walmer causing amazing damage. Within two minutes it was gone.

Oak trees at Coldblow were pulled out of the ground and others turned round on their roots. Slates and tiles were picked up by the wind and deposited hundreds of yards away. Ships at anchor lost their rigging. Much of this was discovered later in the fields of Upper Walmer. Farm buildings were demolished and many animals were killed or had to be destroyed

afterwards.

The tornado had swept in from the sea. In its path were the two public houses, the Cambridge Arms, now the Drum Major, and the Granville Arms. The Cambridge lost all its windows and pictures were sucked out and blown into the sea. The Granville had its roof prised into the air and it crashed down onto the foreshore.

As the tornado passed over Walmer beach it picked up a galley punt and dropped it in the sea. It was later recovered off Ramsgate. With its energy gone the tornado became a hiss of salty spray and disappeared into nothing.

The Lord Warden of the Cinque Ports, Earl Granville, called in a London scientist to examine the phenomena. He calculated the breadth of the storm was never greater than 700 feet and never less than 450 feet and it travelled at a speed of 20 miles an hour.

The blizzard of Tuesday 18th January, 1881 was accompanied by a great storm which caused considerable damage in Dover. Photograph shows the Admiralty Pier.

Best Lifeboat in the Kingdom

1852 — 1861

BETWEEN 1852 and 1861 there was a series of great gales off the Ramsgate coast. Coxswain James Hogben and the crew of the lifeboat Northumberland were instrumental in saving the lives of more than 150 from a variety of shipwrecks. The Lifeboat Institution reported in 1856; "There is no lifeboat in the Kingdom which has been brought so constantly into requisition during the last two years and none that is kept in a greater state of efficiency or more constant readiness for instantaneous service than she is, under the superintendence of the vigilant harbour master at Ramsgate, Captain K.B. Martin."

Snowfall in October

20th October, 1880

OCTOBER snow that settles is almost unheard of during the twentieth century but between 1800 and 1900 there were several notable falls. It lay for five days in 1836 but the outstanding example took place in the cold and very wet month of October 1880. Overnight and during the morning of the 20th, snow fell thickly and built up an enormous weight on the still verdant trees and shrubs. All around Sevenoaks limbs were shed from mighty oaks and elms and sent crashing to the ground. The depth of snow was said to have reached a foot, oustanding even in mid-winter. There was very little wind.

Whirlwind at Birling

6th August, 1885

A whirlwind which hit the village of Birling, near Rochester at 5.30pm on 6th August, 1885 was described in the parish magazine by the vicar of All Saints Church, the Rev. Madden: "The whirlwind came from the south-east and when I first saw it, it looked like a long black woolly funnel or pillar stretching from the clouds to the earth and twisting rapidly round and we all thought it was a water spout. Then we noticed a terrible roaring and as the pillar advanced we saw it was a whirling mass of dust and leaves and boughs. It seemed to cover a space of about 15 yards in width and after it had passed there was dead calm."

Great Victorian Blizzard

18th January, 1881

THE blizzard of 18th January, 1881 ranks as one of the mightiest ever known in the South East of England. Trains were buried in 16 feet of snow, 100 barges were sunk on the Thames alone and several lives were lost.

The sea had rarely behaved so angrily. Shops and houses were awash and all along the Kent coast widespread destruction was reported.

In Sittingbourne and Faversham it was chronicled that "the worst snow-storm ever seen in the district occurred, accompanied by an extraordinary high, gusty, easterly wind which prevailed throughout the day. The snow was perfectly blinding and drifted to an alarming extent. All the country roads are completely blocked, many above the hedgerows, to a height of six or eight feet and many country residences are hemmed in by huge mountains of snow".

At Dover the storm reached its intensity between noon and 1pm and was "blowing a terrific hurricane, so great being its force that it was impossible to stand on the road anywhere near the Rifle's Monument and many persons on crossing to the shelter of the end of the first block of Waterloo Crescent were driven against the fences on the opposite side".

At Canterbury "the snow fell heavily and was drifted by almost a whirlwind into every sheltered spot".

Transport of every kind was paralysed and even the poor inhabitants of Sutton at Hone, near Dartford, had to go without their parochial relief supplies of bread because the "conveyances containing the bread were brought to a standstill from the great depths of snow encountered in each direction".

At Erith 150 men "with commendable alacrity" battled to liberate the district from its snowy imprisonment. Drifts up to 16 feet deep also posed a challenge for the gangs of gentlemen assembled to cut a way between Court Leet Bottom and Bexleyheath, Welling and Crayford.

During the storm Erith was badly flooded and the High Street was inundated. At Crayford Miss Conyard, an assistant teacher at the Slade's Green School, sank up to her chest in a drift and had to be rescued. Unable to extricate herself she was trapped in the snow for more than two hours until Coldstream Guard Thomas Doxberry heard her cries and went to her aid.

At Bexleyheath the body of 24-year-old George Martin was found under a corn stack in a field at Brampton Road.

In the North Woolwich area 26 barges were sunk and in one of them three men were reported drowned. Two dock constables were also missing, feared drowned and two more were lost at Albert Docks.

An estimated £2 million of damage occurred to property along the River Thames as the water surged through defences. The swollen river contained boulders of ice which bombarded buildings, making the damage worse.

Post Office telegraphs between London and the Kent towns were suspended and mail vessels were unable to leave ports.

The 11.30am train from Ramsgate to Dover was snowed up mid way between the two stations. The trapped passengers were led out and conveyed to the nearest communities by road. Only one South Eastern train reached Margate on 18th and two on the Chatham and Dover line. As the gale continued with "unmitigating fury", another train was embedded in a drift near Broadstairs and at Dover part of the railway leading to the South Pier was so damaged that trains could not run.

Between Sittingbourne and Sheerness the railway was obliterated and the train which left Sittingbourne at 9am was halted at Queensborough by the snow and was not heard of for a considerable period. Several trains had to be dug out between Sittingbourne and Faversham.

At Folkestone half the promenade was washed away and a large amount of destruction occurred. "Pedestrianism was so dangerous that the streets were perfectly deserted." In the harbour the most dramatic scene for 40 years was witnessed. The sea "dashed with the utmost fury over the vast pier and breakwater". The corner where the gun stood was completely destroyed and the gun itself buried under the debris.

One of the most remarkable events occurred at Erith where a floating clubhouse, The Gipsey, was seen to be sinking. Just three minutes after the occupants were led off by the river police, the craft sank in "three or four fathoms of water".

The snowstorm was described as the worst since Christmas Day, 1836 in Ashford and certainly such a spectacle has been seen rarely since.

From the beginning of the thaw on 26th January to 5th February the weather was described as "exceedingly fine and mild". On Sunday the 6th the wind veered from the south west to the north east and the day was cold and sunny. There was still much snow lying about and the frost gave a crisp covering before a "terrific gale" on Monday the 7th brought a fresh supply.

The storm on 18th January was caused by a depression which moved from the Bay of Biscay to the Isle of Wight, turned south to France and then headed north east. All the time southern Britain had been in the cold region of the low pressure.

The Medway Valley, either side of Tonbridge, flooded frequently and often the river invaded the town itself as this photograph, taken in the autumn of 1880, shows. It was the floods which determined the modern shape of Tonbridge and the 20th century buildings have been to the north and south, extending the old High Street, rather than along the banks of the river.

Strange Sensation

10th June, 1889

A huge pile of boulders on the foreshore of Sandown attracted great interest among residents between the hours of 12 and one o'clock on 10th June, 1889. The time is important for they were uncovered by the tide following a furious gale and moments later covered up, never to be seen again. This is how Mr Henry Chapman, a former mayor of Deal and witness to this "weird and strange sensation" described the event at the beginning of the century.

"After this disastrous gale the wind suddenly veered round to the north-east, causing an unusually high tide. The fury of the waves was such that the foam rose to the tops of the highest houses and the new sea wall collapsed. Some feet below the coping of the present Marina Parade I saw this layer of huge, smooth, oval-shaped boulders which had been revealed there during the height of the storm. A few hours later the boulders ceased to be on view. The next incoming tide brought back the gravel and the incline on the foreshore was quickly reformed. They may never be seen again, possibly for a thousand years."

Snow in July

THE year 1888 was extraordinary in many ways. Apart from 1879, it is ranked as the coldest of the past 150 years. On 19th March a severe powdery, drifting snowstorm blocked railway cuttings in East Kent and overwhelmed the streets of Dover.

July was probably one of the most dismal summer months of the nineteenth century. At Tenterden it was the wettest July on record. It was especially notable for a bitterly cold day on the 11th when early in the morning it actually snowed at Cudham. At Canterbury it resulted in the ground being covered for a while.

Erith's visitor

Erith has seen many boisterous winters but the gale of January 1886 was one of unusual severity — unusual because it lasted just a few seconds but long enough to inflict serious damage on a number of homes, including Reydon Lodge in Lesney Park Road which lost part of its roof. The storm moved south eastwards, sweeping down from north west Birmingham, where it hit at 9am, through Stratford-upon-Avon to reach Erith at 11am.

The straits of Dover have frequently been compared with the thoroughfare in London between Hyde Park Corner and the Haymarket. Up and down "Piccadilly Circus" go ships of every nation — warships, carriers, tankers, liners and ferries. Throughout history the beaches have been the last resting place of many great ships but among the most famous was the wreck of the Firth of Cromarty, grounded in St. Mary's Bay in January 1894 during a "fearful gale". The Cromarty, a full-rigged wind jammer of 1,400 tons loaded with cement and canned goods, was driven ashore and heavy seas broke over her incessantly. The Coastguards attempted to rescue the crew by means of the rocket apparatus and all were saved apart from one seaman and a poor lad who was apprentice on his first voyage. While he was being hauled ashore he was so exhausted that he slipped away and was drowned.

The great frost of 1895 froze the River Thames at Gravesend. Ships were icebound for many days.

When the Thames was Frozen

February 1895

SKATERS thronged the frozen River Medway, animals shivered to death in the fields and starving people joined the free soup and bread queues throughout the Medway towns as the Great Frost tightened its grip in February 1895.

The Medway was frozen from shore to shore for nearly a fortnight and river traffic was brought to a standstill. Almost all outdoor work in the Medway towns was impossible and, as a result, thousands of men were put out of work.

A Chatham News reporter wrote: "The scene today was extremely touching; the hungry poor assembling in great crowds and fighting their way to the doors in their struggles to get bread." Near Romney Marsh, a Mrs Sayer ran one such soup kitchen. "She begged marrow bones and odd bits from the butcher and dried peas, beans and oatmeal from the grocers; dunned the farmers for turnips and added a good deal from her own household."

The intense cold brought tragedy. At Sheerness a barge mate was frozen to death and near Maidstone a father of six was drowned in the icy waters of the Medway when the ice broke as he skated.

February 9th was one of the coldest days of the last two centuries, with the mercury failing to rise above 23F (-5C) in town centres by day and remaining even lower in country areas. On this day shipping was almost at a standstill and at Gravesend ice covered the Thames. The first ship to feel the grip of the ice was the Dutch Amstelstroom from Amsterdam. She was "quite unable to proceed to her berth at the Pool and

put into Tilbury Docks", the Gravesend Reporter noted.

Scores of barges came drifting down the river, together with the ice floes. Customs and pilots' services were badly affected. Children were magnetised to the river to watch the wintry scenes. Some hopped on to ice "bergs" and emulated scenes from the book Uncle Tom's Cabin. At night flare lamps were lit to enable the skating to continue on the Gravesend and Higham canal. These lighter moments in the freeze were often overshadowed by the grim events which hit the headlines. A prison warder was frozen to death at his post in Chatham and at Chatham Dockyard a policeman named Westrip nearly followed suit while walking back to the Medway towns from the Leather Bottle Inn at Cobham. Ironically, he was rescued by a fellow constable called Tom Frost.

Many ships, big and small, were damaged by ice. The yacht Gem sank off Strood pier and the steam yacht Casilda was written off. The deputy governor of nearby Borstal prison and his son and daughter fell through the ice while skating but were rescued by a Royal Engineer Officer.

On the Medway barge men walked across the ice to and from their vessels stranded in midstream and some pulled each other across on sledges. Before the river froze up completely the Arctic exploration vessel, Discovery, ploughed its way into Chatham through the ice floes in an operation more suited to its earlier journeys.

On 28th September, 1896 the enterprising Folkestone Herald produced a special four-page supplement describing "yesterday's hurricane" which was "without parallel in the memory of the present generation". At the height of the gale two vessels were seen in distress off the Victoria Pier and the gallant crew of the Hythe Lifeboat went to the rescue. The shipwrecked mariners from The Agdar were quickly saved but the lifeboat was temporarily disabled and the crew of the Baron Holberg (pictured above) suffered an "interval of unspeakable anguish, fearful that the masts of their sinking ship would crash down with fatal results". Thousands of spectators lined up on the beach and The Leas to watch the drama. They saw the lifeboat repaired and, amid deafening shouts of acclamation, watched another "exhibition of indomitable bravery by the intrepid coastmen". All were saved.

Margate 'Changed For Ever'

29th November, 1897

MANY great tides, which sweep out of the north gaining height and momentum on their journey south, have hit the Kent coastline between the Thames estuary and the Thanet peninsular. Few have been more destructive than the tidal surge which struck the towns of Herne Bay, Whitstable, Margate, Broadstairs, Westgate-on-Sea and Birchington on 29th November, 1897. The tide was accompanied by a cyclonic disturbance which increased in violence to hurricane force and then unleashed its full fury on the Thanet towns.

Sea walls, coastal defences, buildings and roadways were washed away. The tides rolled against the towns destroying the promenade at Westgate, the colonnade, erected 24 years earlier, at Ramsgate and breaching the pier at Broadstairs. In Margate the Marine Palace was destroyed, the jetty, stone pier and Droit office seriously damaged and the massive sea wall was eroded causing huge fissures in the cliff face. The newspaper known as Keble's Margate and Ramsgate Gazette wrote that "the havoc wrought by wind and sea presents a melancholy testimony of their overwhelming power. Not even that useful and unveracious person the oldest inhabitant possessed memories of a tempest which has brought such widespread ruin. Although the storms of 1808 and 1846 were destructive they were trivial compared to this and it is hardly an exaggeration to say that the face of Margate has been changed forever". The reporter, with Victorian eloquence continued: "Through the mist of the spray, huge masses of water could be seen rising mountain-like, their created summits roaring in a majestic splendour high above their prey and in the thunders of sea and wind the work of the rain went on until the ebbing of the tide stayed their pitiless fury."

This was the scene at Margate Harbour when the funeral of the Margate Surfboat disaster victims was held. The service was held at the parish church of St John.

Nine Drown in Surfboat Disaster

2nd December, 1897

IT was five o'clock on the morning of 2nd December, 1897 and the "Thanet storm" had still not abated when the coastguard on duty at The Pier reported distress signals from a ship on the other side of Margate Sands.

The surfboat Friends to All Nations along with the lifeboat Quiver set off to the aid of the stricken vessel. It was blowing heavily from NNW with sudden and severe squalls of rain and hail, when the surfboat inexplicably overturned. Out of 13 men on the boat nine were drowned. The news of the disaster quickly swept through the Thanet town which was soon in a state of deep shock. This is how the newspaper Keble's Margate described the tragedy in its next issue.

"One of the most lamentable and disastrous events which has overtaken Margate for many years, occurred in the early hours of Thursday morning (2nd December) by the passing of the Margate surfboat Friend to All Nations. Out of a full complement of 13

men, including Mr C.E. Troughton, superintendent of the Margate ambulance corps, who invariably accompanied one or other of the boats on their errands of mercy, only four were saved. No such shocking and appalling catastrophe has happened at Margate since the eventful 5th January, 1857 when the lugger Victory was lost with her crew of nine hands. The sad event following on only three days after the great storm and accompanying destruction of property made this week in the year 1897 one that will be long remembered in the history of Margate.

"How the accident happened was scarcely known to the survivors, and what really caused this usually staunch little craft to turn turtle is to a great extent a matter of conjecture. It was stated, on the authority of one of the survivors, that the sail was being lowered when a sudden squall struck them "all of a heap", filled the bulging sail with water and, in that way, brought about this most deplorable accident.

In August, 1898 the want of water was becoming serious. At Tenterden there was a great deficiency of water in springs, wells and ponds. At Birchington, September was the driest month ever remembered. Our photograph shows Orpington Ponds on the only known occasion, at that time, when the headwaters of the River Cray had dried up.

Competing for the 'Sunshine Market'

ALTHOUGH there were 12 summers of below-average temperatures in the last quarter of the nineteenth century, it did not stop the holiday trade from becoming Kent's most flourishing and highly developed industry. Every coastal town from Sheerness round to Littlestone competed for a share in the "sunshine" market. Councils, local businessmen and outside investors built piers, promenades, hotels, theatres and even new towns. Letting houses and landladies, ice cream and candyfloss, bathing huts and amusement arcades cropped up everywhere.

By 1900 Margate was a well-established holiday resort for it had been fashionable for wealthy Londoners to make use of the regular Hoy service down the Thames. Herne Bay owed its popularity to the railway which arrived in the early 1860s and Folkestone to its designation as a cross-Channel port in 1843. Whitstable, offering shrimp teas and simple attractions, was an early favourite and Dover attracted those on a day excursion on the London Chatham railway.

For the day trippers and the longer stayers August was always the most popular month, due in the main to school holidays but also to the additional day off — Bank Holiday Monday which had been introduced in

1871. The warmest sea water in England in August is the Channel which averages about 63F (17C) and has always attracted the cheerful hordes. At the turn of the century only a fraction of the working class could afford the time or the money for an extended visit and most crammed everything they could into the "day trip".

Although the boom years of the late 1890s were accompanied by some cool summers, there were exceptions. The spring of 1893 had no rain in places for 50 consecutive days or more and that, of course, constituted a drought. The late summer of 1898 was extremely hot and the Victorians flocked to the seaside, especially to Folkestone which was then indisputably the most fashionable resort in the county.

In the boom years most people in Kent went to one of the Kentish seaside towns for their summer holidays or an occasional day trip. They went in search of that well-advertised sunshine and discovered also, winds in excess of 100 mph, mist and fog, drenching deluges, tidal waves, floods and, on one occasion, summer snow. The weather has played a memorable role in the varying fortunes of all our seaside towns.

February 17, 1900 and Dartford is under water again. Traders and travellers had to endure many great floods in the town centre before and after the turn of the century.

Little Venice on the River Darent

DARTFORD, positioned vulnerably on the Thames Estuary and mouth of the River Darent, once flooded so frequently that it was affectionately known by those who lived in North Kent as a — "little Venice".

There are certainly no gondoliers in Dartford but on many occasions a river has run down the main shopping streets, lapping the front doors of shops, offices and homes. Industry has suffered badly but Dartfordians, have taken each calamity in their stride, cleared up the mess and then prayed for a lengthy immunity from the next disaster. It has never been long coming.

There would have been many floods in the middle ages but the first to command the attention of bygone writers was in 1814 when the lower portions of the town were under several feet of water and the entire floor of the church was covered by three feet. It was the same in 1866 when water was seen to be rising from the "Cran-Pit" stream in the High Street. The Cran-Pit rises a few miles above Dartford and passes along the valley reaching the town on the eastern side of Lowfield Street where it divides into two arms. One travels under Waterside to the Creek; the other diverges toward the river and runs under the High Street opposite the church.

On 12th April, 1878 the Dartford Chronicle reported that Lowfield Street and Hythe Street were "complete rivers and every branching and declining aperture at the east side, a torrent. In 22 hours the rainfall was officially given as nearly three inches".

It was the "Great Flood of 1900" which finally prompted the Dartford Chronicle to urge the authorities to take precautions. "The town from its natural position will always suffer in time of flood and it is remarkable that some steps have not been taken to lessen the danger arising", it stated.

"Late on Friday (23rd February, 1900) it was seen that the water was rising rapidly and a flood was anticipated but very few were they who dreamt of such a state of things as was ours to experience on the day following. The large volume of water which had flooded the low-lying lands of Eynsford, Farningham and Darenth was gradually moving towards Dartford. By eleven o'clock in the evening the water had crossed the street near the church and rapidly rose. By the early hours of the morning large portions of the town were submerged and the next day brought a suspension in trade and all the usual chaos."

Edwardian Notes

1900: Heavy rain and melting snow led to widespread flooding in February. Five and a half inches (137 mm) fell at Ospringe. July brought a heatwave with an absolute drought of 23 days at Birchington and a temperature of 91F (33C) at Tenterden.

1904: Six inches of snow fell at Dover on 1st March.

A fierce hailstorm at Broomy Farm, Colling on 27th August stripped leaves from apple trees and smashed the fruit. The equivalent of 2.66 inches (68 mm) of rain fell in just 45 minutes. Only an area 500 yards by 300 yards was affected.

1905: A hop picker was killed by lightning at Leigh on 27th August.

1906: A remarkable storm on 10th February combined lightning, loud peals of thunder, snow, sleet and heavy rain to cause great damage throughout Kent. Windmills at Challock and Frindsbury were set on fire by lightning, which also struck the steeple of the 700-year-old church at Westwell, causing a fireball to slide down the tower. As the church blazed, Ashford Fire Brigade were called and, for several hours, pumped water from the nearby lake until the fire was under control.

There was great heat in early September, above 90F (32C) and heavy snow on Christmas night.

1908: Several inches of snow fell on the Kent and Surrey border on 24th April. In the village of Brasted, the branches of firs were bent double with their burden of snow and a correspondent to the village magazine wrote that this was the heaviest April snowstorm since 1860 when lambs had to be dug out of drifts.

1909: The depth of snow reached 19 inches in early March at Maidstone.

Skating on the millpond at Tenterden during February, 1902.

Dust storm at Edenbridge, 1903

Much of Kent had its wettest year on record but February was warm and dry. At Edenbridge an unusual phenomenon occurred. A fall of dust mixed with light rain adorned shrubs and trees with a murky covering. The temperature was high for the time of year and the humidity low, indicative of the desert origin of the air. The wind carried the dust to a great height and much of southern England was affected, although the Edenbridge fall was exceptional.

"A freak of nature", reads the caption to this old postcard. "A chestnut tree on Birling Common with new leaves — October 18, 1906". It was certainly an unusual year with a chill spring, a moderate summer and then, in September, temperatures in excess of 90F (32.2C). Nature was confused. Buds formed again on some trees and by October spring was in the air!

A whirlwind, which attacked the village of Sholden near Deal on the morning of 25th November, 1907, lasted little more than 10 minutes but inflicted enormous damage to Orchard Farm owned by Mr George Wellard. The whirlwind arrived at six in the morning. At one moment there was a normal November breeze blowing over the fields. The next, without any warning, the wind increased in speed to more than 80 miles an hour and the barometer plunged. Everywhere there was confusion. Roofs disappeared from farm buildings and a huge centre beam from one outhouse was carried some distance before it came to rest against a cottage chimney stack. A haystack was lifted off the ground and landed on the deck of a Russian ship at anchor near the Goodwin Sands, covering the men with straw.

An exhilarating game of curling is in progress on the Military Canal at Hythe, frozen solid in the winter of 1908-9.

This is the single horse footpath snow-plough on duty in Folkestone in March 1909 when it snowed without interruption for 36 hours. This was the new age of the combustion engine and many motorists had not experienced the imcompatibility of car and snow, especially on Sandgate Hill. In the town centre the only sign of life was the huddled, overcoated figure of the local PC on point duty. When the snow stopped, the first detachment of workers emerged before dawn with six single horse footpath snow-ploughs followed by one roadplough with six horses. Together, they helped to liberate Folkestone.

Two events caused great excitement in Folkestone — the October floods of 1909 and the arrival of a photographer. Here a great crowd gathers to watch the men pump out water from the cellars of The Imperial.

The Wild, Destructive Pent

26th October, 1909

FOR many centuries the east coast of Kent has been a battleground in the unceasing conflict between land and sea but when Folkestone was flooded on 26th October, 1909 the waves were not to blame. It was caused by torrential rain. In three extraordinary days 5.99 inches (153 mm) fell, turning the harmless little brook The Pent into a wild, destructive fast-flowing river.

The Pent trickles down from the hills, under Tontine Street, to the harbour but the rains augmented its strength and, according to the Folkestone Herald, caused it to "burst its confines and show its ancient powers".

The newspaper continued: "The event will remain an abiding memory in the minds of the residents of Folkestone and Foord. The hours of the night were hours of horror as the raging waters forced people to the doubtful security of upstairs apartments."

On the first night there was the sound of the incessant rain beating against window panes and then the voices of policemen warning people of the dangers around them. Outside, rivers ran in Russell Road. Wat-

kin Road, Bonsor Road and the valley of Foord. Pavilion Road was awash with waves which crashed against the walls of the shops. Residents, abandoning their homes, linked arms to cross the torrents and then look for refuge on higher ground.

One man described how he was saved from certain death. Mr John Bedwell of 24 Young's Road said at the time: "I was sleeping in the basement and, at 12.15, I was awakened by hearing the wall at the back of the house falling down. The water started coming in. I tried to open the door to get out but could not do so owing to the force of the water. Then I went to the front door, jammed my foot in it and tried to push. The force of the swirling water was too much. I was a prisoner and the water was rising. For 20 minutes I watched the water rise from my knees to my neck, all the time calling for help. At the last moment three men heard my cries and came to the rescue".

Hundreds of Folkestone people were made homeless by the floods. They were partially comforted by the proceeds from a relief fund which was opened in the town by the mayor.

The floods of October, 1909 caused great excitement in Canterbury where the river was reported to be roaring through the town at a tremendous rate and had "never been higher". In St Peter's Lane the water flowed into the front doors. The whole of the district between Canterbury and Fordwich had the appearance of an inroad of the sea and the Stour Valley was one expanse of water. The photograph (above) shows four boys in a broken down cart and (below) a horse and cart providing transport in St Radigunds. while (right) duck boards keep feet dry.

Maidstone was flooded twice in 1909 and would have presented scenes in the High Street very similar to this. As this picture is undated it could also have been taken in the great flood of February 17th, 1900 when the floodwater from the Medway and the Len reached one of its highest levels ever.

Canterbury swelters at 98F

1911

THE winter of 1910-11 was relatively benign but winter sometimes has the habit of putting in a late appearance, outbearing the old Scandinavian saying "as the day lengthens so the cold strengthens".

A bitter wind from the north-east blew in late March, accompanied by squalls of snow. At Folkestone a brick wall some 60 feet long was blown down on the 25th and the storm reached its peak during the evening, causing the demise of many a telephone line on Sheppey. The island became cut off from the outside world for a time.

April became even colder and a ferocious easterly gale on the 5th, laden with snow, led to terrible losses to lambs, fruit and potatoes in the fields south of Chatham and Sittingbourne. With the mercury hovering at freezing point, huge icicles festooned buildings in Rochester. Deep drifts impeded all forms of

transport and the Staplehurst mail cart took nearly six hours to travel seven miles from Maidstone to Chatham.

July and August brought some of the best weather our islands have ever seen. By 9th August the temperature had soared to 95F (35C) at Tenterden as hot air was drawn off the Continent and at Canterbury a sweltering 98F (37C) was recorded which was, until 1990, the hottest reading Britain has ever registered.

Great heat and drought continued into September but an active weather system on the 12th accompanied by a sudden squall at Tunbridge Wells, heralded more seasonal weather. This was followed by a very wet late autumn and winter and boats were out on the streets of Tonbridge in November as the Medway burst its banks.

On 22nd March, 1913 Hythe was battered by a storm which pulverised the promenade. The photograph shows the damage looking down the coast towards Dymchurch.

Unrest on the Weather Front

1912: A remarkable glaze occurred on 17th January. At Chatham and Gravesend trees were heavily coated with ice. Rain fell and froze immediately. At night a Lawson Cypress reflected a thousand little points of light from a street lamp.

In Dover large numbers of "telegraphic" poles and wires came crashing to the ground under the sheer weight of ice.

In April no rain fell in Bromley but August was the wettest on record.

1913: Rain and thunderstorms caused heavy flooding in Old Folkestone on 30th August. Water levels rose with alarming rapidity in basements and cellars. It poured off Shorncliffe like a cataract straight through several cottages. Tons of gravel washed down covering the tram tracks and suspending the service.

1914: During the evening of 28th December a severe gale with gusts to hurricane force unroofed many buildings and blew down trees at Langley near Maidstone.

1916: Heavy snow fell in late February, reaching a depth of eight inches on Bromley Common. It continued into March with a foot on the 7th. An observer at West Wickham said the snowflakes were the largest he had ever seen, measuring a full four inches across.

1917: After a cold winter and spring, when Keston had 16 days of snow in April, rain fell almost incessantly over east Kent between 29th July and 3rd August. This included one spell when it rained for 54 hours non-stop. Part of Canterbury recorded 10 inches (250 mm) representing nearly six months' rain. Villages such as Chilham, Detling and Bicknor had eight inches. The total amount in the area was enough to fill 11 million average sized municipal swimming pools! It was during this period that Britons, fighting in the third battle of Ypres on the other side of the Channel, became bogged down in the Flanders mud after remorseless rainstorms.

25th May, 1922 and workmen at Southborough remove hailstones from the main road.

Glaziers were Busy for Weeks

25th May, 1922

HAILSTONES, the size and shape of tangerines, which fell on Tunbridge Wells and the surrounding area on the afternoon of 25th May, 1922, smashed so many shop and office windows that local suppliers ran out of replacement glass and hundreds of tons had to be ordered from London. Glaziers were busy for weeks.

This phenomenal storm came up the valley of the Weald, passed over the elevated ground at Southborough, drove down into "The Wells", built up over the ridge of hills at Hawkenbury and vented its wrath on the town, not even passing beyond as far as half way to Frant.

The violence which lasted just 15 minutes was described by the Tunbridge Wells Advertiser as a terrifying experience. "The thunderous rattle of enormous hailstones, the smashing of glass in all directions, the scattering of foliage and branches everywhere and the flooding of the low-lying thoroughfares created a scene of pandemonium which will remain crystaline in the memories of everyone.

"Never before have the local glaziers been so heavily taxed to meet the orders which simply poured in for the replacement of broken glass. Messrs Hobbs and Son received orders which will enable them to dispose of no less than eight tons of glass, one order alone being for 800 panes. The biggest order was for 1,200 panes at Sherington Hall, Speldhurst, yet a quarter of a mile away not a single pane was destroyed.

"R.W. Weekes probably suffered the most as a result of their premises being flooded. The rushing waters quickly overflowed the pavement and, reaching a height of more than two feet, found its way through the doors of the large showroom and thereafter flowed into the basement where a vast amount of valuable stock is stored. Damage is estimated at £1,000."

Mr D.W. Horner, a Fellow of the Royal Meteorological Society wrote at the time that the amount of water that descended on Tunbridge Wells in a quarter of an hour was 100 tons on the acre at Calverley Park and 108 tons per acre at Hawkenbury — a "truly phenonemal storm".

The metal plate covering the boot of this car was bombarded by hailstones which caused several indentations.

A crowd gathers at the entrance to the famous Pantiles in Tunbridge Wells where many stores were flooded and stock badly damaged.

4th January, 1925 and Dartford town centre is invaded again by water from the River Darent which flooded shops and cellars, keeping the fire brigade busy for hours. In a letter to the Dartford Chronicle, a correspondent wrote: "A chain is as strong as its weakest link and similarly the carrying capacity of the Darent is determined by the foulest part of the river. Between Hawley and Darenth the river consists of 20 per cent water and 80 per cent mud and in times of heavy rain it is a frequent occurrence for people in these villages, and Sutton at Hone, to be cut off from their place of work. Let us clean out the bed of the Darent through its entire course of 17 miles from Westerham to Dartford, allow it to function properly and save our beautiful Darenth Valley from these inundations".

The Desert Town of Margate

1921

HIGH air pressure almost invariably brings dry weather and sometimes it can persist for several weeks at a time. In 1921 a wedge of high pressure stretched north-east from the Azores towards southern England and remained for most of the year. The result was an exceptionally low annual rainfall, the like of which had not been seen since the eighteenth century.

Along the shores of the Thames estuary and North Kent coast less than 10 inches (250mm) of rain fell with the lowest ever yearly total measured anywhere in the British Isles (a mere 9.29 inches, 236mm recorded at Margate). A desert is usually defined as having less than 10 inches annually, so for one year Margate was the Sahara of Britain.

Remarkably, in the same year, Loan in Invernesshire was swept by moisture-laden winds coming straight off the Atlantic. By the end of December the rain gauge there had been working overtime, measuring an amazing 202 inches (5125mm) - more than enough to fill a deep swimming pool. In Kent barely enough rain fell to cover one's ankles.

A Bus to The Barge

January 1925

A photograph taken in early January of Bennett's Bus in Wittersham Road, Rolvenden Layne during the first floods of 1925. More flooding occurred in February when most of the low lying villages in Kent were under several feet of water. The cause was an intense rainstorm which raged without cessation the whole of Saturday 13th February. The most serious damage occurred in the Medway valley. At Maidstone, Messrs Masons Brewery was flooded and at Tonbridge, the municipal sports ground was a massive lake. In the Stour Valley between Chartham and Canterbury and on Romney Marsh, graziers had an anxious task get-

ting their stock into safe quarters. As usual the whole of the Rother Valley was deeply flooded. Wittersham, "capital" of the Isle of Oxney, was an island once again, approachable only by boat and at Newenden the inhabitants were prisoners in their own home.

Flood waters also lapped right up to the front door of Ellen Terry's house in Smallhythe, which was once the harbourmaster's house, when the sea ran in as far as this. Regulars who wished to visit the Barge Inn in Rolvenden Layne, just round the corner from where this picture was taken, had a damp walk. Floods or no floods, there was always Mr Bennett's splendid bus!

Drama on Boxing Day

1927-1928

CHRISTMAS Day 1927 was miserable. Rain lashed down for hours, the roads were muddy and by the late afternoon there was a chill in the air. As the family festivities continued into the evening with teas, games and charades, outside Mother Nature was unveiling the biggest drama of all.

Although the temperature had climbed to 46F (8C) earlier in the day, a cutting north easterly wind had stormed into the southern counties and turned the heavy rain to driving, blinding snow.

The Boxing Day Blizzard was to become one of the county's worst snow-storms of the century. On the North Downs at Biggin Hill, houses were buried up to their roofs. Near Hubbards Hill, Sevenoaks Weald, the snow was whipped into drifts 18 feet deep and near Tatsfield, bungalow dwellers were imprisoned in their homes. Motor cars were completely covered and many roads were indistinguishable from their whitened surroundings.

At Polhill, near Sevenoaks, the snow lay 15 feet deep in places and the road was totally out of bounds, with several cars buried. The East Surrey and West Kent bus services were unable to operate and trains were also badly hit.

On Boxing Day evening a Farningham omnibus, which had been diverted, and a Maidstone bus became embedded in the snow on Seal Chart and many passengers were stranded.

Comedian Wilkie Bard was motoring to Maidstone with his wife when he became stuck in deep snow at Wrotham Hill. They, along with 20 others, became involuntary prisoners for nearly a week at the Clearway tea rooms - a rather inept title on that day. Food started to run out by 30th December, so oil barrels were smashed to make sledges and an expedition party organised to search for provisions. On Boxing Day evening, the gale force north-easterly wind snapped the flagstaff on Seal Church and it crashed to the ground. Two days later masses of snow above the railway cutting between Kemsing and Otford collapsed on to the tracks, holding up trains for three hours. Serious drifts also occurred at Chelsfield and gangs of railwaymen engaged in clearing the line often had to run hurriedly out of the way as avalanches roared down the embankments.

Villages high on the Downs were cut off for a week and on Thursday 29th December a light aircraft took off from Stag Lane Aerodrome with supplies of food to drop on marooned communities around Biggin Hill and Westerham.

The BBC asked people to lay out black clothes in the snow "not less than 15 feet in diameter" to help pilots pin-point people in need. On 31st December the Salvation Army chartered five aeroplanes to drop supplies to isolated villages.

Some of the most dramatic stories came from Biggin Hill, 600 feet above sea level, where the snow in places had drifted up to the top rooms of houses and nine people were imprisoned in one bungalow. As fast as they tried to dig their way out, the snow piled up again. One man who attempted to reach the trapped people fell into a drift up to his neck and only saved himself by clinging on to a tree branch.

A rescue party set out to try and release Biggin Hill from its icy grip. They found the road over Keston Common completely "lost" and reported that the snow around Biggin Hill was up to 18 feet deep. One householder at Biggin Hill gave a warm welcome to the search party and told them they were the first people from the outside world they had seen since Christmas night. He feared that if the gale did not cease their houses would be completely buried under snow.

The east of Kent escaped the worst of the snowstorms and parts of the county towards the North Sea had only heavy rain. Three inches (76mm) of rain fell between Ashford and Dover on 25th and 26th.

At New Bridge on the Tenterden road, the River Beult rose 12 feet on Boxing Day night and was above the coping of the bridge. The next day both a Maidstone and a London bus were trapped in the middle and had to be towed out by horses.

A fire tender was used to help a well-known tradesman get to his premises in the lower part of High Street, Maidstone by way of a bedroom window.

Floods struck the area more generally as the snows melted, and scores of homes in Brasted and Westerham were under water. Mrs Smith of Rectory Lane, Brasted was resting by the fireside with her feet up when she heard a call. On opening the door a huge wave of water surged through her home and she had to be carried through a foot of muddy water.

At Sundridge the village milk float ferried people to the station because of nine inches of flood water on the approach roads.

1928: On January 6th the Thames burst its banks, drowning 14 people including four sisters in their basement home. Hundreds became homeless in North Kent on the banks of the swollen river. The disaster was caused by a combination of the thaw, following the blizzard of December, 1927 and an extremely high tide.

Somehow the bus from London to Rye has managed to get as far as Dunton Green, near the foot of Polhill,
but the Boxing Day snow-drifts bar the way and no further progress is made.

The village of Downe near Biggin Hill, the home of Charles Darwin, was completely cut off by the Boxing Day blizzard. The photograph shows The Queen's Head, almost buried in snow.

A street lamp in Maidstone is almost submerged — ample proof of the depth and severity of the 1927 floods.

This is Canterbury, 1927. Two stretcher-bearers carry a patient through the floods to their waiting ambulance.

Canterbury's Catastrophe

26th December, 1927

NEWSPAPERS all over England were full of stories of the heroism, resolution and ingenuity that had accompanied the memorable Boxing Day blizzard. But in East Kent, particularly in Maidstone and Canterbury, there was far more to worry about than the effects of a mere snow-storm. Both towns were under water, hundreds of people were homeless and relief funds were under way to meet the most tragic of demands.

It was the same storm. The depression from the Atlantic which had moved from Ireland to the English Channel brought snow to West Kent and, to the east of Maidstone, heavy rain. In fact the rain was so intense that rivers quickly burst their banks and flood waters rose at an alarming rate. The people of Canterbury had experienced many inundations but, on this occasion, it was necessary for the Mayor to launch an appeal for funds in what was, arguably, the City's greatest natural disaster.

A souvenir newspaper called "Canterbury's Catastrophe" was published. "None of us realised when we retired to bed on Boxing Night that the morning would find many homes ruined by water and the inmates penned into their quarters without food or firing", wrote the mayor. "In a season of rejoicing and festivity, when everyone was looking to happy family gatherings and additional comforts, many have spent their holiday cooped up in bedrooms with the swirling waters beneath them doing havoc to their homes".

In St Peter's Place, water was too deep for a horse and cart to approach. All the boats had been sunk by the floods except for one which conveyed milk, tea and biscuits to the marooned people. The Salvation Army sent to Whitstable for more boats and managed to secure one for every flooded street. In Broad Oak Road people had lived on bread and butter for two days.

The newspaper had a special message for future scribes. "When the history of this flood comes to be written, the sterling work of the corporation officials and workmen will be found to have deserved well of all. They operated relief carts, soup vans and boats and worked long hours in the bitter cold. The workmen in waders who made contact with houses on foot had a no less unpleasant task which was discharged in the true British spirit."

A resident of St Peter's Place, Canterbury rescues his four-month-old baby from the upper windows of his home. This was one of hundreds of houses flooded in the city in December, 1927. Just over a week later, the combination of a sudden thaw and abnormal tides caused the Thames to burst its banks, flooding every acre between Rotherhithe and Gravesend. Hundreds of houses were damaged and people needed special assistance. So quickly did the waters rise that fourteen people drowned in London, including four young sisters and thousands of people were made homeless along the length of the grey, swollen river.

Three men walk across the frozen waves at Whitstable in February, 1929, one of the coldest Februaries of the century. During this period the ice on Lake Windermere was reported to have borne the weight of 50,000 skaters. By June, the country was basking in a heat-wave.

THE four schoolgirls are drawing a strictly rationed water supply from the village well at Toys Hill, near Edenbridge in July, 1929 during one of England's most prolonged droughts. In fact, so serious a menace to health and labour had the drought become, that on 19th July — the 136th rainless day of that year — the Metropolitan Water Board suspended the use of water for gardens and motor cars. The Board also informed consumers that they were liable for penalties for waste, misuse or undue consumption.

Although there were many dry days in April, May and June 1929, the real problem was traced back to February and March when, in many areas of Kent, it rained on just two occasions and reservoirs and rivers were already low when the summer began.

During 1929 meteorologists were talking about the possibility of a new record for successive days without rain. But this was not to be. In fact it fell a long way short of the record achieved in the spring drought of 1893 when some places in Kent had no rain for 50 consecutive days or more.

Ramsgate in the late twenties when the hotels and boarding houses were mostly full and the terraces, gardens, pavilion and pier were packed with those enjoying a holiday by the sea. As always, the most popular place was the beach.

A Glance at the Twenties

1920: A very mild winter led to an observation at West Wickham that asparagus was cut on 26th March, the earliest date known, with tulips, lilies-of-the valley and all perennials well advanced.

1922: On 22nd May, Bexleyheath sweltered in 90F (32C). This was the earliest date of any year such a figure had been reached.

1923: A nightmare for brontophobics as an all-night storm on 9th-10th July recorded over 6,000 flashes of lightning. Beckenham and Hayes had over two inches of rain (50 mm).

1924: A thunderstorm on 26th September led to streets being awash with floodwater at Dartford.

1925: During a violent south-westerly in the Straits of Dover during January, huge breakers swept away hundreds of tons of shingle from the beach at St Margaret's Bay. Bathing huts and tents, left on the

beach from the previous summer, were washed out to sea and then rescued by boatmen.

1926: A severe thunderstorm at Ramsgate overnight on 16th August caused thousands of pounds worth of damage. At Bossingham crops and fruit trees were ruined by hailstones. Martello Tower Number Three on Folkestone's East Cliff was struck by lightning and badly damaged.

1929: During February and March persistently dense fog in the Channel brought all the noises associated with danger for ships. Sirens, foghorns and maroons were consistently being sounded and the people of Deal found it difficult to sleep. In these conditions the German steamship Oliva crashed head-on into the South Goodwin light-vessel. The Deal motor boat, Lady Beatty, was launched in answer to distress signals and found the vessel, badly damaged, but still afloat. All were rescued.

The River Medway, swollen again by heavy rains, flooded villages and towns in November 1935. Many areas were entirely cut off and villagers had to be rescued from their homes and placed in a cart. The farm horse then plodded on to the next flooded home. The picture, taken at Fowle Hall, Paddock Wood shows the local rescue team carrying a young lady and a small boy to safety. The popular BBC wireless programme In Town Tonight carried a special feature on the Paddock Wood floods when millions of listeners all over the world heard Mr Jack Parker describe how he had delivered the mail during the great floods of 1909. He then outlined the various ordeals faced by those who lived on the riverside of the Medway.

Fog, Frost, Floods — and Kentish Mists

THE photograph on the right shows a veil of early-morning mist draping itself across the Darenth Valley at Shoreham near the point where the railway line taking Kent commuters to London disappears into the long tunnel under the North Downs. On their return visit in the evening, the same travellers will burst out of the blackness and the Metropolis into the bright, clear Kentish air where all around there are open fields and orchards. This photograph was taken in the early autumn of 1939 from the top of Polhill, long before the arrival of the M25, long before the Great Storm of 1987 removed all the trees and many years before we said goodbye to the magnificent age of steam. Towards the east, rising above the mist, is Otford Mount.

Railwaymen are not too concerned about the early-morning Kentish mists. It is fog, frost and floods which they fear — conditions which have caused, over the years, many accidents and fatalities on the railways.

On 24th January, 1846 the flooded bridge between Penshurst and Tonbridge collapsed into the Medway in the middle of the night. A train ran off the end of the line into the river. The driver, Charles Dolby, was trapped between the engine and tender but the fireman managed to drag him out and swim to the bank. Mr Dolby, however, did not survive.

In February, 1856 a "hurricane" caused extensive damage to the railway line at Dover and the following autumn the sea encroached on to the Dover Town station platforms. A sum of £4,000 had to be spent reinforcing the sea defences.

In March, 1869 sea encroachment caused a serious slip on the line through Folkestone Warren and, along the cliffs, 16 coastguard houses were damaged.

In 1873 a porter was killed at Tonbridge station when he tried to put lamps into the carriages. He climbed onto the roof but fell as the train began to move. Snow had made the surface icy and he was run over by the tender and three carriages.

The South Eastern Railway was faced with many problems in Dover caused by the violent storm of 14th November, 1875. The groynes outside the Lord Warden Hotel were wrecked, most of the station roof caved in and the tracks were awash. The Admiralty Pier signalbox "disappeared" and its telegraph instrument was later found in the inner harbour.

The winter of 1876-7 was exceptionally wet with around 18 inches (450mm) of rain in West Kent during December and January. The gales of New Year's Day had a catastrophic effect. The Dover goods shed was smashed to pieces, the line from Dover station onto the pier was undermined and tracks in the station yard were rendered unusable.

On 21st March, 1898, in thick fog, a serious accident occurred at St John's, Lewisham when the 7.45 am up train from Tonbridge was hit in the rear by the 7 am up from Hastings. Three people were killed instantly and more than 20 injured. Almost 60 years later, on 4th December, 1957, fog caused an even worse disaster on this line when 92 people died. See page 93.

Ancient and modern tackle Kentish floods together on 23rd January, 1937. The location remains a mystery.

Just over a month after the outbreak of war, the front-line town of Folkestone found itself coping with a not-too-unexpected disaster. Heavy rains caused the Pent Stream to overflow and many streets were awash with swirling water. The photograph was taken in Ashley Avenue, Cheriton on 28th October, 1939.

Snippets From The Thirties

1930: A severe gale struck West Kent during the evening of Sunday, 12th January. Bromley Common was littered with fallen trees and there was turmoil around the church at Keston as winds exceeded 70 mph. Several huge elms fell at Holwood Park.

1931: Frequent spells of snow on the Downs of West Kent in early March. Several inches on Hayes Common with day temperatures only 27F (-3C).

1933: A fine summer with Margate reaching 94F (34C) but December was cold with a mean of just above freezing at Tunbridge Wells.

1934: A violent thunderstorm on 22nd July caused a landslide onto the railway track between West Wickham and Hayes and a train just managed to avoid ploughing into it. Rainfall was so heavy as to form an almost impenetrable curtain with 4.70 inches (120 mm) falling at West Wickham. Near Beckenham 100 cars broke down in the flood waters.

1936: On 16th December Appledore Church was struck by lightning and the weather vane damaged. At nearby Newchurch, 12 sheep were killed.

1938: A classic white Christmas with snow every day from 18th December and only a maximum of 22F (-6C) at Lympne on 21st.

1939: A remarkable turnabout in the normal pattern of weather took place in October. The Highlands of Scotland stayed dry whilst Margate recorded 10.28 inches (261 mm) of rain, an inch more than fell during the whole year in 1921!

War Postponed by Blizzards

January 1940

SECRECY surrounded the wild winter of 1940 and for several weeks news of the vicious cold and snow could not be broadcast for fear the information could be useful to the enemy.

It was the same all over Europe, for every country, even Portugal and Spain, was held in the icy grip of one of the severest frosts on record and the expected German attack on the Western Front did not materialise because of the weather. At home, towns and villages were marooned, supplies of food and fuel were running dangerously low and the threat of unemployment added to the misery.

The cold weather set in at the tail end of December, 1939 and carried out a merciless campaign for six weeks, checked only on the odd day or two by brief incursions of milder air from the west. Snow, whipped up by piercing winds from the east, heaped into huge drifts which covered the tops of hedgerows.

Author C Henry Warren wrote, in his book England is a Village, vivid descriptions of the cold spell in Larkfield, a fictionalised name for the sake of wartime secrecy, but which could have applied to any small village in Kent. In early January he recalled how the war had almost been forgotten because of the sensational weather at home.

"During these last seven days, the war for most of us, has been little more than a not very substantial rumour penetrating our homes by radio and occasionally by news-paper.

"For days we, a community of some 900 souls hud-dled together in a white waste of snow, have been almost cut off from the outside world."

He related how the elderly folk of 'Larkfield' had always boasted of the great blizzard of January, 1881 and had made comparisons. They had told the younger folk that, in 1881, the snow had been so deep it was possible to walk over the tops of hedges, but the incredulous children could not imagine it. Not in the kindly south they thought. The young villagers credited their tales to the proneness of old people to exaggerate the happenings of years gone by. That is until they were overwhelmed by the snows of January 1940.

The 'Larkfield' diarist commented on the behaviour of the people around him as the freeze tightened its grip.

"It is one of the merits of village life, as well as one of the penalties, that we are, even in the most propitious days, so closely interdependent on one another. And, when such inclement weather shuts us away from the world, we are even more closely united.

If there was kindness among us before, it is more than trebled now. If there was envy, hatred or malice, it seems for the moment to have been forgotten. Perhaps there is an element of fear compelling us to this unstinted kindness; a faint echo in us of the days when, to an extent that not even the severest hardships can inspire today, men and women were forced to find safety in communal endeavour. Or perhaps it is nothing more than excitement engendered by a spectacle in which, whether we will or no, we are compelled to play a part."

"The same dead sky hangs over us all, day after day. The same snow comes flaking down on the just and the unjust alike. And the same uncanny silence fills us all, even the most unsusceptible among us with the premonitions of we know not what."

In spite of the hardships brought to Kent by the perishing cold, there were scenes of great beauty in the countryside as the drifts were sculptured into weird and wonderful shapes by the wind.

At Gilbert's Rise, 'Larkield', the snow was heaped "as high as a haystack". But the picturesque scenes brought little comfort to the villagers. Foodstuffs could not get through and the mail van did not arrive for several days on end. This did not stop the 'Larkfield' postmistress, Miss Dickson, from opening her store. Those who stepped inside experienced "her jocular manner and her warm-hearted concern for the welfare of us all".

It was several weeks after the freeze before news of it was allowed to be published by the Air Ministry. On 21st March, The Times published a letter from a weather observer giving details of the intense cold.

The article stated that, at the height of the bitter weather, on 20th January, Canterbury had experienced a bone-chilling temperature of -4F (-20C) or 36 degrees of frost to the older generation. No wonder the Thames froze to the south west of London and the sea froze at Whitstable. This turned out to be one of the coldest nights of the century in Kent.

Canterbury's overall temperature for the month was 28.4F (-2C) and over the whole country generally the month was the coldest of any January since 1881.

When the snow and ice melted, around 4th February, the inevitable floods struck. In the village of Ash, water cascaded down from the hills above,"throwing off a spray". At Darenth, roads were under a foot of water and at Sutton at Hone sacks of potatoes were used to divert the floods from Mr Chaplin's farm.

On 9th February the winds returned and once again Kent was gripped by a severe frost. The first winter of the war would not give up without a fight.

Snow in Kent, but ssh it's a Secret

JANUARY, 1940. This photograph of a three-horse snowplough negotiating the narrow lanes in the hills above Otford would have been published in local newspapers some weeks after it was taken. Due to the war all reference to the weather was censored for 15 days. So, although Kent like the rest of Britain and Europe shivered in the coldest spell since 1895, nothing was written about the snow-drifts which blocked most roads in the county until the following month.

Later in 1940, after the evacuation of Dunkirk, a German invasion was anticipated and signposts in Kent were removed. It is possible that these crossroads, not far from the fighter station at Biggin Hill, would have become anonymous until the war ended. In East Kent a foot of snow fell in an hour and drifts were severe - certainly the wrong conditions for flying or fighting!

As the snows of 1940 rapidly thawed, a new menace hit many low-lying Kentish villages — floods. It was particularly bad in the Cray Valley where several people moved into upstairs rooms waiting to be rescued. Our photograph shows a smiling lady from Green Street Green, sitting on her dining room chair, in the safe hands of the Orpington Auxiliary Fire Service. Nearby, her husband courageously wades through the swirling water. By 4th February, 1940 many villages in North Kent were under water and advertisements were placed in the local newspapers offering to deliver groceries to marooned people in St Mary's Cray, St Paul's Cray, Chelsfield, Pratts Bottom and Well Hill. At Crockenhill there was a landslide.

With the Battle of Britain raging overhead, there was work to be done in the hop gardens of Kent. This young lady is hop picking at Beltring, near Paddock Wood. She carries a gas mask over her arm.

Blue Skies for Battle of Britain

The summer of 1940

ON occasions, a winter of blizzards, snow-drifts and frozen seas has been followed by a damp spring and then long summer days when the sun beats down from a cloudless sky and the countryside looks at its best. Such a year was 1940 — the year our troops were evacuated from the beaches of Dunkirk and the year the RAF won the Battle of Britain. The Kentish weather played a memorable part.

Operation Dynamo, the evacuation of the British Expeditionary Forces, took place between 29th May and 4th June, 1940 when more than 338,000 troops, two thirds of them British, were snatched from what threatened to be the biggest military disaster in the history of Great Britain.

There were many factors which made possible this "miracle of deliverance", including the brave resistance on the perimeter, the supreme efforts of the naval vessels and "little ships" and the contribution of the RAF who flew 2,739 fighter sorties during the evacuation. However, there was poor visibility in the Channel and in the Kentish harbours on four of the days and the blanket of mist thwarted the efforts of the Luftwaffe to stop the mission.

Following Dunkirk, June was full of warm, sun-bathed days when the lawns and even the flower beds of all the Kentish fighter stations - Biggin Hill, Manston, Hawkinge, West Malling, Lympne and Rochester - were in perfect trim. In July there were a few "dirty" days with fog, low cloud and intermittent summer rain. Many young pilots were briefed for a sortie and then, after one look at the weather reports, drank an early morning cup of tea and returned for a lie-in.

The July weather improved dramatically. Scudding clouds thinned to reveal rapidly growing patches of blue and the great aerial battles began in earnest with the Luftwaffe keen to wipe the RAF from the skies as a preliminary to the invasion of Britain. In August the clouds returned briefly giving the commanders on both sides pause for reflection and reconsideration and to modify their order for battle.

Then came the brilliant clear days of September when the barometer remained high and the skies were often blue. In these conditions the people of Kent saw the Battle of Britain reach its zenith, the whirling patterns of vapour trails in the sky depicting a dance of life or death. Day after glorious day the pilots, cocooned in their cockpits, climbed into the rising thermals from a sun-baked earth as they strove for precious height. Eventually the Luftwaffe threat was repulsed and the Germans scurried back to their bases leaving a parched Kent countryside littered with the smoking wrecks of aircraft. The battle raged on through the clear autumnal days of October until Hitler postponed his invasion of Britain.

A mined Dutch cargo ship, Nora, grounded at Deal, was swept by gales and tides in 1939 against Deal Pier, which split, twisted and finally broke. Other piers were purposely divided in 1940 so the enemy could not use them as landing stages during the danger from invasion.

A double decker bus full of passengers travelling from Wrotham to Gravesend on 3rd March, 1946 in the most appalling conditions skidded off the road at Meopham and almost overturned. No-one was injured. On the road, abandoned, are an army lorry and a private car.

The War Years and Beyond

1940: At Lympne there were 12 ice days (below freezing) in January whilst at night, over a deep snow cover, a chilling 2F (-17C) was measured at Wye and Whitstable.

1941-42: For three consecutive winters it was snowy and Preston, near Faversham, had 43 days of snow cover in the winter of 1942.

1944-45: Kent recorded Britain's maximum temperature in these two years, with Tunbridge Wells and Whitstable reaching over 90F (32C).

1946: A vivid display of the Aurora Borealis during the night of 23rd-24th April.

1947: In this legendary winter, Kent's lowest official temperature was recorded at Elmstone: -6F (-21C) on 29th January.

1948: In a mild winter a short but severe icy spell in February gave 11 inches of snow at Wilmington and 14 inches at Biggin Hill. The snow gradually melted as two weeks of fine, sunny weather followed.

1949: On 17th April at Whitstable early holiday-makers experienced a summerlike heatwave with 82F (28C).

The Bleak Winter of 1947

WITH food and fuel still scarce following the war, the one thing people dreaded was a hard winter. Trying to keep homes warm with so little coal available was a miserable task and many fireplaces were stacked up with broken furniture or even shoes to keep the embers glowing.

By the third week of January, people hoped they had escaped any evil tricks the weather might have had in store but as the winds swung into the east on the 23rd, winter arrived with a vengeance as bitterly cold air surged in from the continent. Blizzards, sub zero temperatures and seemingly endless grey skies brought great hardships for several weeks. This served as a double blow, for the county was already shivering as a result of the enforced power cuts in homes and places of work.

The Gravesend and Dartford Reporter of 1st February told how one foot of level snow had fallen in the Medway Valley on top of the snowfall of the previous days. Parts of the River Medway had frozen over and at West Malling the temperature had fallen to a perishing 3F (-16C) on 28th January and to just 1F (-17C) at Teynham.

Snow, whipped up by the icy winds, piled into drifts six feet deep, dislocating traffic on many roads. Gangs using snow-ploughs battled with teams of German prisoners of war to keep roads clear. The village of Trottiscliffe was cut off and had to be dug out and a similar story emerged from Nurstead where a party had to shovel their way through "five feet of hard snow" to reach the inhabitants.

The Isle of Sheppey was cut off from the mainland and the light railway to Leysdown was snowed under. Milkmen had to use sledges rather than their horses or handcarts to deliver milk to schools and homes.

A Gravesend shopkeeper walking in from near Buckland had a frightening experience when she couldn't tell where the roads ended and the hedgerows began. Suddenly she sank up to her shoulders in a drift and nearly disappeared.

In Folkestone, danger signs were put up on either side of the town hall because of the icicles — many pounds in weight — which adorned the side of the building.

On Saturday 25th January, the attendance at the Stonebridge Road football ground, Northfleet, was just 250 instead of the usual 5,000. The following week's inspection revealed six foot snowdrifts on the ground.

At Gravesend magistrates court, the temperature one morning stood at only 30F (-1C). The Gravesend Reporter declared that it was a "disgusting state of affairs.

"While others in the court turn a delicate shade of purple with the cold, the only warm people are the magistrates who sit in comfortable chairs and toast their toes at a battery of electric heaters."

The freezing weather was linked to the death of several people. The body of a man aged 24 was found covered with snow in a house under construction in Linden Avenue near the Princes Road in Dartford.

The snowstorms stopped all shipping in the Channel around 12th February stengthening fears of greater food shortages to follow. Many fishing fleets were forced to stay in port and only three of the usual 42 aircraft landed at London's three airports on that day.

Industry was thrown into confusion by the power-cuts during off-peak periods and hundreds were laid off. Electricity to homes was cut during the mornings and afternoons. Even Buckingham Palace and the Ministry Offices were candle-lit. At Hythe brewery, a bottling plant was operated by hand to get beer into bottles before it went bad.

Oil lamps were used to light the stage at the Tonbridge Grammar School for Girls when pupils performed Shakespeare's Winter's Tale "but this added to the atmosphere", said the Tonbridge Free Press.

Parts of the South East had their coldest readings this century on the still, starry night of 23rd February, with Tunbridge Wells recording -2F (-19C).

The lack of sunshine earlier in the month added to the misery of the winter. For almost three weeks the sun had failed to come out at all until blue, alpine conditions prevailed from 23rd to 26th.

Some people believe that with the arrival of March comes cheerful spring weather but this was far from the case in 1947. There were two more weeks of snow-falls, rain and frost and before the mild weather arrived some of the worst conditions of the winter seized up the county. Rain fell on to the frozen ground, coating everything with a layer of ice. Trees, telephone wires and poles, hedges and even houses were encased in the glassy layer. The Folkestone Herald commented: "Nothing escaped the ice. Even the tiniest blade of grass had its coating.

"Telephone wires sagged to the ground under the weight of ice and pulled down poles. Trees collapsed and branches snapped off."

Warmer weather finally took over on 16th. The temperature soared to 57F (14C) near the Thames and, combined with continuing heavy rain and gale force winds, the thaw led to widespread flooding.

1949: Serious flooding between Margate and Gravesend on 1st March caused by exceptional high tide. As flood waters engulfed more and more areas, Kent Fire Brigade received hundreds of calls for assistance from every town and village along the north Kent coast. So bad was the flooding that Herne Bay, Whitstable and Chatham had to be declared 'one incident'.

An ice breaker in action on the River Medway at Allington, near Maidstone.

In March, 1947 at Bridgewood, between Maidstone and Chatham, it was still possible to walk over snow-drifts.

A desolate scene in Bexleyheath in February, 1948 when the trolley buses became welded to the overhead conductor rails.

Year with a Lot of Weather

AFTER the severe cold of January and February, followed by gales and floods in March, the weather again made the headlines, this time for heat and drought during the summer and autumn of 1947.

It was not all blue sky and sun as thunder clouds gathered at times and West Malling twice received two inches of rain with lightning striking an aircraft and building on 18th July.

At Lympne there was an excess of 62 sunshine hours on June's average values but it was August that stole the limelight. It was the warmest on record over England as a whole when the mercury rose to 80F (27C) even in the far north of Scotland at Cape Wrath. As in the bitter month of February, high pressure gave

easterly winds across Kent but this time they brought dry and often sunny weather. The drought lasted for 50 days at Wye.

October continued the dry theme with less than half an inch of rain and it became very warm with 75F (24C) at Wilmington on the 13th. There was some interesting weather in November, too. A cold spell mid-month with a little snow was suddenly pushed away by a flood of warm humid air from southerly latitudes, making the insides of many buildings wet with condensation. It became spring-like on the 23rd with 60F (16C) by day, falling only a few degrees at night.

On Christmas Day thunder was heard over some parts of Kent, to round off quite an unusual year.

The AA motorbike was the only vehicle mobile on this stretch of the blizzard-swept A20 road near Wrotham on 21st February, 1948. The scout is pictured here at the height of the storm giving assistance to a bus and several vehicles which had come to a standstill. Deep powder snow fell over much of Kent during the three days from 20th February.

Flares to Guide the Buses

30th November, 1948

IT was Tuesday afternoon on 30th November, 1948 when the fog closed in on London and North Kent for the third consecutive day. This time it was thicker than ever. Buses, trams and trolleys ground to a halt and men carrying flares helped to guide them to the depot in Bexleyheath. Hundreds of City workers left their offices in order to catch an early train home. Many were unlucky — few were running. Arsenal workers at Woolwich downed their tools and set off on their journey home, by Shanks's Pony! Shops closed early. Evening papers, Standard, News and Star, failed to arrive. By dusk, the roads were virtually deserted.

Or were they? On the main road, near Sidcup, barely visible in the pea-soup conditions, two unusual shapes were causing some anxiety among those who dared to inch their way through the gloom. The shapes turned out to be horses who had somehow escaped from their stables and were lost in the fog. Two Sidcup policemen were called, the animals were "arrested" and led to the lock up.

For five days the fog enveloped all of London and much of Kent. The Woolwich Ferry stopped running, attendances at schools were down, cinemas and restaurants closed, cyclists found it safer to walk, Saturday and Sunday sports fixtures were cancelled, dinner speakers failed to turn up and there were numerous minor accidents.

At Gravel Hill, Bexleyheath a man carrying a flare preceded a convoy of vehicles travelling at snail's pace towards the Rochester Way. At Plumstead a woman walking home in the fog lost her little dog. For two hours she called his name and, in tears, gave up her search. When she arrived home the dog was patiently waiting by the front door. He hadn't needed a flare to guide him home!

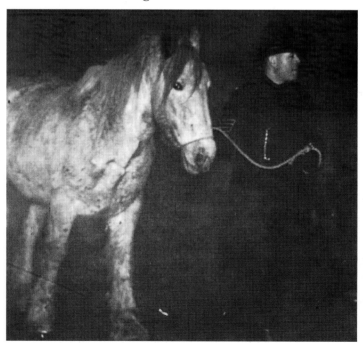

The village of Hastingleigh, near Ashford was isolated when drifts, some of them nearly 10 feet high, blocked all roads leading to the village. Snow-ploughs had little effect as high winds blew more snow from the fields. However, on Monday morning, 23rd February, 1948, ten hardy villagers and ten Ministry of Transport employees set to work to dig themselves out. It took the men two days to reach the Brabourne-Waltham crossroads, where the welcome party included a photographer.

Serious flooding between Margate and Gravesend was caused by strong winds and an exceptionally high tide in March, 1949. As flood waters engulfed more and more areas, Kent Fire Brigade received calls for assistance from every town, village and hamlet along the North Kent coast. So bad was the flooding that Herne Bay, Whitstable and Chatham were described by the firemen as "one incident". This photograph taken by Chris Fright shows the huge waves battering the promenade at Margate.

In North Kent the Cray Valley once again burst its banks and there was a scramble for sandbags to protect hundreds of homes in imminent danger of flooding. Here are the sandbaggers!

From the Well, Strictly Rationed

TWO years after the "Mediterranean summer" of 1947, Kent wilted in the heat once again. Day after day throughout June and July the sun bore down on to a parched earth, straining the resources of the Kent Fire Brigade whose men could hardly believe what was happening. A few months earlier they had been dealing with widespread coastal floods. Rivers ran dry, water was strictly rationed and heathland and forest fires became widespread.

In many areas of Kent the most vital commodity was still drawn from wells where the water levels dropped lower and lower. Our photograph was taken near Ide Hill, a sun-baked village gloriously placed on the greensand ridge near Sevenoaks, where there was a well on the village green and in several private gardens. The five sweltering people queueing for water at Brook Cottage, Ide Hill include Harry Schultz (with the jug), an ex-prisoner of war who stayed and worked in the village, Ron Pattinson, Mrs Pattinson and her daughter, Rose who was to marry Harry Schultz. It was taken on 28th June, 1949.

This long, hot summer brought the total calls to Kent Fire Brigade to a new record of 8,636. More than 900 fires in the county were caused by trains setting fire to grass embankments and hedgerows. Urgent requests were made to British Rail to create fire breaks and fit spark arresters on steam locomotives, unfortunately without result.

Caffyns Garage in Sevenoaks after the roof had fallen in under the weight of the "spring" snow-fall. Many cars inside the garage were badly damaged

Even The Cuckoo Was Confused

26th April, 1950

"OH to be in England now that April's here." Certainly those who lived in West Kent in April 1950 appreciated Robert Browning's words and their good fortune.

By the 22nd the sun was shining, tulips were in profusion and the cuckoo was in fine voice. Four days later the flowers were under a foot of snow and the cuckoo was covered in confusion.

A polar depression had crossed over south-east England, tugging down Arctic air and turning heavy rain into a snow-storm in the early hours of Wednesday 26th April. By 7am numerous trees were lying across the road. Every main road leading into Sevenoaks was blocked. Telegraph poles were snapped in half at Tonbridge. Buses and cars were skidding off snow-covered roads in Westerham and Biggin Hill. Around Orpington traffic became entangled in icy wires.

At Sevenoaks the roof of Caffyns Garage at Tubs Hill gave way under the weight of snow and crashed down onto the tops of cars causing thousands of pounds worth of damage. The Sevenoaks Chronicle wrote: "In years to come old men will tell their grandchildren the story of Wednesday 26th April in the year of Grace, 1950. And the grandchildren will refuse, perhaps, to believe that all this was due to a six-hour fall of snow,

two weeks after "summer time" had arrived."

The driver of a Sainsbury's van on his way to Bexhill had an amazing escape on Polhill between Sevenoaks and Orpington. As he was descending the hill he saw a tree in front of him come crashing down. He pulled up in time as it came to earth just in front of his radiator. He was looking behind to see if the way was clear for reversing when another tree came down imprisoning the van but, fortunately, missing it.

A woman living near Weald village looked out of her bedroom window and saw what looked like an aeroplane resting against the roof of her house. It was, in fact, a large birch tree in full leaf, forced down by the volume and weight of snow.

The extraordinary blizzard caused such serious damage that questions were asked in the House of Commons. Members were told that the snow contained a lot of water and it was the weight which caused so much destruction. Many trees were in leaf when they toppled, paralysing road and railway services to London.

By the weekend, gangs of workmen had cleared trees from main roads and engineers from many parts of the country were helping local crews restore telephone supplies.

The heavy clinging snow brought down hundreds of miles of telephone wires in Kent. This photograph was taken at Hayes Common, near Bromley where a telegraph pole was snapped in half.

This was the scene at Polhill, near Sevenoaks on the morning of 26th April, 1950 where large trees had been uprooted by the heavy and unexpected fall of snow. Thirty seven years later this hillside was to be stripped completely of its trees in the great storm of October 1987.

Bromley Enjoys Dry October

OCTOBER is normally one of the wettest months of the year but on occasions it can boast long dry spells, such as in 1947 and again in 1950. Bromley enjoyed 23 dry days with only 0.3 inch (8mm) of rain. High pressure predominated for most of the month.

It was all change in November, with low pressure and storm centres passing over or close to Kent. On the 10th, nearly an inch fell in just 12 hours at Lympne and rainfall totals topped 6 inches (160mm) in places for the month.

When Sidcup Hill became ice-bound on 4th December, 1950, some 64 buses were baulked on the hill and could not move until gangs arrived with gravel and made the going safe. This picture shows the glaze glistening on the road and buses lined-up all the way down the hill.

Pure Farce, but this wasn't Funny

4th December, 1950

IT was a freezing December evening and the roads in Bromley were glistening as a cyclist came out of Bromley South station, took his bicycle from the rack and made his way carefully down the hill. Before he reached the bottom he was sprawling in the middle of the road. Another cyclist joined him on the deck. Then another, and another. It was pure farce and the cab drivers waiting outside the station could hardly control their mirth.

This was no laughing matter. The cause of the mishaps was glaze, a rare weather phenomenon, when snow turned to freezing rain and coated all roads with ice. It coincided with the evening rush hour and the laughing taxi drivers soon had the smile wiped off their faces as they saw buses going sideways and pedestrians sliding uncontrollably on the pavements. The Bromley Times wrote: "The cabbies stood at the end of the slope warning cyclists to get off their machines. Most of them took no notice and in five

minutes there were 34 spills on that stretch of road alone".

At Beckenham a bus descending the treacherous hill skidded and collided with three stationary cars. In other areas bus drivers refused to continue. On Masons Hill there was a great traffic jam with cars across the road in all kinds of different angles. On Bromley Hill a lorry mounted the pavement, knocking down a lamp standard. Trains were also affected and some almost welded themselves to the conductor rails. Accidents were caused by people not realising the dangers. Even the most cautious drivers would put their foot on the brakes only to find their cars skating gently on.

The casualty ward at Bromley Hospital had a busy evening. The local newspaper reported: "Broken collar bones were the most common injury but there were a number with broken arms, cuts and bruises."

Another victim of the ice-bound roads in December 1950 was a 401 bus travelling to Upper Belvedere which skidded broadside near Farningham. There was plenty of help at hand.

Weather in the Fifties

1951: One of the greatest weather-related tragedies in Kent's history occurred at Chatham on 4th December when, in thick fog, a bus ploughed into a company of Marine Cadets. Twenty three youngsters were killed.

1952: A French steam ship, The Agen, laden with mahogany was stranded on the eastern edge of the Goodwin Sands at the height of a full gale and broke in two. The Walmer Lifeboat went to the rescue and Coxswain Fred Upton took it through the 30 feet gap separating the two parts of the ship no less than three times in order to save The Agen's master. Although the crew was saved, the master refused to abandon his command and, only after he had spent a night on board his sinking ship alone, did he consent to be taken off. The rescue brought Fred Upton and the Walmer crew more medals for bravery.

1953: Following the east coast disaster, the hurricane force winds of February along the north Kent coast were replaced by a six-day foggy spell in mid March. On a cold, wet, cheerless day on 2nd June, thousands of people travelled to London to stand for hours on the footpaths. The occasion was the Coronation of Queen Elizabeth and among those in the procession was Queen Salote of Tonga, a huge beaming figure who waved vigorously to the crowds as her carriage filled with rain water.

1955: In a year which saw the UK's heaviest ever 24-hour rainfall of 11 inches (279 mm) in Dorset, Kent experienced several thunderstorms and in August a landslide blocked the London to Folkestone road at Sittingbourne and the Bredgar Post Office was flooded.

1956: During February low temperatures and deep snow swept Kent, with readings of 2F (-17C) at Wye and the day maximum at Dartford just 23F (-5C). Ice formed along the coast and piled up a foot thick in places between Dungeness and Greatstone on Romney Marsh. Thousands of seagulls were driven shorewards by the bitter weather. Snow reached a depth of 15 inches and drifts were so bad that Kent County Council had to enlist military assistance to keep the roads clear.

1959: A glorious summer was followed by a heatwave in early October with the temperature 82F (28C) at Dartford.

On the day that Oxford won the Boat Race in blizzard conditions, Kent's most famous resident was attempting to find a way through the snow-drifts at Biggin Hill to his home at Chartwell. But this was a battle Mr Winston Churchill was to lose. His car was abandoned and he was driven home in another vehicle by a more circuitous route. The picture above shows the scene on Monday morning, 31st March 1952 with men shovelling snow from the main road between Westerham and Biggin Hill while the driver and conductor of the local bus look on anxiously. All around them cars were buried in snow-drifts. The Sevenoaks Chronicle wrote that one had to see the drifts to believe the size of them. No attempt had been made to bulldoze snow from the London and Croydon roads out of Westerham and the only activity was provided by gangs of men with shovels. Among them was a Metropolitan policeman who attempted to release the Prime Minister's car before he, too, gave up the task.

Hundreds die in London "smog"

5th-8th December, 1952

NO-ONE knows exactly how many died as a direct result of the London Fog of 5th-8th December, 1952, but in the two weeks following the greatest mass killing of the century, the death rate in Greater London rose by more than 4,000 and many were Kentish people living by or near the industrial banks of the Thames.

It was on Thursday 4th December, 1952 that a fog warning was given on the wireless. At first the fog was not that dense but of a dry, smoky character. The next night, however, came the real water fog, which is the basis of all great London smogs. It was a genuine "pea-souper". With visibility only a few yards, traffic, by road and rail, was reduced to chaos.

On the nights of Saturday, Sunday and Monday it was impossible for pedestrians to move about in familiar surroundings. From Deptford, along the industrial North Kent embankments, to Erith, the visibility was reduced to almost nil. In dockland areas it was said that "one couldn't see one's feet"!

Those living near, or passing by, factories and power houses suffered violent fits of coughing. Animals, particularly cattle, were asphixiated. The fog contained localised pockets of a highly poisonous nature due to the concentration of sulphur dioxide and associated gases emanating from factory chimneys and slowly drifting along in the sluggish circulation of the watery blanket. Newspapers described the event as "London's Great Smog" — the type known to those of the last century as a filthy, black Victorian "pea-souper" and thought to be virtually extinct. People trapped in poisonous pockets suffered an irritation of the respiratory system caused by the joint effect of sulphur dioxide, smoke and perhaps other irritants. The coughing and vomiting led to heart failure and in those two weeks in Greater London approximately 8,000 people died - nearly double the normal death rate of around 2,000 per week.

Tidal Surge Claims Many Lives

31st January-1st February, 1953

ON 31st January, 1953 a storm surge, driven by hurricane-force north-westerly winds crashed against the east coast sea defences causing widespread flooding and extensive damage to more than 1,000 miles of coastline.

In this most catastrophic event of the century, the waters of the North Sea were whipped up to massive tidal levels which then smashed through sea wall fortifications, breaching more than 1,200 sites. Whole communities were isolated, 32,000 people had to be evacuated from their homes and 307 lost their lives.

The storm began with a deep depression which moved east-north-east from south of Iceland and then turned rapidly south-east into the North Sea, while pressure rose rapidly to the west, producing a steep pressure gradient. In England the gales were accompanied by heavy driving rain and low cloud and the wind speed exceeded 75 miles an hour.

Flooding began on the Northumberland coast at 4 pm on Saturday 31st January and during the following nine hours, 1,200 miles of sea and tidal defences were attacked in turn, extending as far south as the Isle of Thanet.

The North Kent coast, unlike Essex and parts of East Anglia, is fully exposed to the fury of north and north-westerly gales and, on this unforgettable night, the whole length of the Kent coastline from Woolwich to Birchington was overtopped. There were 400 ruptures, some several hundred yards in length, and in many coastal towns sea water lay up to nine feet deep. Hundreds of acres of farmland were inundated by the sea.

Along the Thames and Medway estuaries industry was thrown out of production for several weeks. Gasworks, power stations and factories suffered immense damage and the consequences to both dairy and arable farms were calamitous.

It was in the early hours of Sunday 1st February, 1953 that an official of the Anglo-Iranian Oil Company on the Isle of Grain noticed, to his horror, that water was pouring over the top of the sea walls into the refinery. Immediately he telephoned the deputy engineer of the Kent River Board which owned most of the North Kent coastline. It was the first indication of the disaster. As the surge attacked sea walls and sand dunes, the archaic defence system totally collapsed and huge waves swept inland, swirling up the estuaries of both the Thames and the Medway. Within minutes, thousands of telephones were out of action, roads were impassable and all communications were severed.

From Woolwich to Margate the storm winds generated a wave action so immense that whole beaches were destroyed, sand dunes swept away and cliff faces eroded.

At Dartford, great holes appeared in the river bank. Water surged through the flood barriers quickly surrounding the Littlebrook Power Station and cutting off the shift workers from the "mainland". At North Reach the water that poured into Joseph Well's fireworks factory generated explosions of such ferocity that windows were blasted out in the town centre.

The people of Kent, in the darkness of their homes, had no idea of the horrors that were unfolding a few miles across the water at Canvey Island. Between 12.30 and 2am the islanders were fighting for their lives and only those who had taken refuge in attics, lofts and on the roofs of their houses were out of danger. Within 15 minutes of the sea wall being breached, water was above window sill level, gushing down streets and spreading in every direction.

The rushing torrent of wind and water carried all before it — outhouses, telephone boxes, front doors and bodies. People died in their beds, others were carried away as the floods rose steadily. One man died clinging to the branches of a tree he had climbed. Many grasped floating furniture and were trapped in deep water for hours before dying of exposure. The death toll on Canvey Island was 58.

Meanwhile, on the Belvedere marshes, a sluice keeper was drowned but, amazingly, he was the only human fatality in Kent. It was the livestock which were to perish in their hundreds and many roads were blocked with the bodies of dead sheep.

The Isle of Sheppey was defenceless. At Sheerness the submarine Sidar was in dry dock when a tidal wave swept over the wall and filled it to a depth of 36 feet. The submarine sank. Alongside it, the bow of the frigate HMS Berkeley Castle was lifted up onto the dock wall amd tipped over. In the lower part of the town, water streamed into homes and the bridge over the River Swale was marooned in an expanse of water four miles wide. Most of the town and half of the island was submerged.

At Whitstable, water simply poured over the top of the new sea wall, which had just been completed, and flowed into homes in the low-lying town. Boathouses were destroyed, vessels were driven by the tide into basement rooms, oyster barrels from the Whitstable Company's store were washed down the streets and shingle was swept into the gardens of homes. At first light rescuers found an elderly couple standing on their kitchen sink helplessly watching the water rise.

For two days and nights this horse was in flood water which covered his entire body. He was eventually rescued from Sheerness on Monday, 2nd February, 1953.

Herne Bay suffered badly. The promenade was buried under thousands of tons of shingle and at one place the road was blocked by a four-foot wall of smashed rowing boats. Sand piled up in the town centre and offices, shops and houses facing the sea were flooded. Not even the urban council offices escaped; water swept into the strong room, located valuable documents and washed them through the town.

At Beltinge, a few miles to the east, the cliff face was furiously attacked by the pounding waves which advanced more than 100 yards inland. A cliff-top road tumbled into the sea along with the gates and large sections of land belonging to the Miramar Hotel. Houses, in imminent danger of collapse, were quickly evacuated.

Between Reculver and Birchington the great northern sea wall was ruptured in many places. The main London to Margate railway line was flooded and, near Birchington, great lengths of rail were swept off the embankment.

At Margate, the sea wall held in most places but gaps were torn in the concrete facing the promenade. The 60-foot lighthouse at the entrance to Margate Harbour was undermined. Those who had left their flooded homes, watched the lighthouse lean at a crazy angle, then fall into the sea. Swirling water swept into the Classic Cinema where, ironically, the film was entitled "Whirlpool". At the height of the gale it was impossible to walk along Marine Drive which was awash. The seaward corners of Westbrook Pavilion were ripped away and the narrow streets leading to the harbour were choked with refuse and broken boats. Shops and homes were awash and the only sign of life in the flooded police station was a drunk who had been inadvertently left in a cell. Late on Saturday evening Margate was blacked out but Dreamland switched on to its own generator and the dancing continued until the early hours of the morning. The band was accompanied by the shrieking wind and the roaring waves outside.

Sea water swept inland as far as Sarre where the villagers wondered if it would cross the main Canterbury Road and flow across the low country to Stonar — making the Isle of Thanet an island once more.

Children help to salvage belongings from their sea-wrecked home in Beach Street, Herne Bay.

All over North Kent there were carcasses of sheep, cows, pigs and chickens, drowned in the first onslaught of water. Some livestock stood about on knolls of land and on what remained of sea walls. Many of these pathetic creatures were rescued by farmers. The famous Kent orchards did not escape either. Some 600 acres of apple, pear and cherry trees were destroyed. Glasshouses were wrecked and every kind of farm enterprise suffered.

At Northfleet, firemen and army personnel evacuated 17 people from their homes as water rose to an alarming level. At the Deep Water Jetty scores of 2cwt barrels of resin, used in the manufacture of paper, were washed away, only to be swept up in the gardens of houses in Stonebridge Road.

Three dogs were all that could be saved from a bungalow under the River Wall at Long Reach. Mr Alfred Shrub was on night duty when the alarm was raised. He was called home to find one of his greyhounds floating in its bed. The following day, the roof was all that could be seen of the house above the water.

In Kent, like other stricken areas along the east coast, gifts poured in from all over the world. Furniture, bedding, fuel, clothes, money, offers of accommodation, sandbags, transport and machinery of every description were freely given by manufacturers, individuals, tradesmen and community clubs in an unprecedented gesture of sympathy and goodwill. Distribution centres for clothes, feeding centres and mobile homes were set up. There was Government help for farmers and there were urgent high level consultations on the need to reinstate tidal defences.

Even before the mopping up had really begun, the 1953 tidal surge had earned a place in history as the most catastrophic weather event of the century. Those who lived through this nightmare were haunted by one single thought — when will it happen again?

Soldiers build a Bailey bridge across pontoons as they strengthen the defences with sandbags near Dartford.

Walking the plank. A couple edge their way to safety as flood waters rise in Whitstable.

71

The harbour offices at Broadstairs receive a visit from another huge wave.

The police station at Margate was evacuated in the early hours of Sunday morning 1st February, 1953. Photographer Chris Fright discovered a "forgotten" drunk in the cells.

A grunt of appreciation as another flood victim is carried to safety, near Dartford.

The famous oasts of Beltring hop farm at East Peckham standing in the middle of an "ocean".

Cars left in the car park of Whitstable Golf Club are just visible above the waterline.

Tidal Surge of 1953

Sheerness Times & Guardian

No. 5095   FRIDAY, FEBRUARY 13, 1953   THREEPENCE

THE ROYAL NAVY CLEARS ROAD TO THE ISLE

"GRAVE RISK" JUSTIFIED

THREE hundred men of the Royal Navy, including explosive experts, took part in blasting operations begun early on Friday morning to clear the Ferry Road and railway lines. Narrow, shallow gaps in the bank were cut to drain off flood water, then several feet deep over the area. Picture shows men blasting gaps in the sea wall on both sides of the Kingsferry Bridge, in an attempt to drain the water back into the sea. A lot of water has been dispersed in this way.

The decision to carry out blasting operations was made by Mr. J. I. Taylor, deputy engineer to the Kent River Board, who has been in charge of emergency operations in the county. The Clerk to the Board, Mr. P. Cox, commented, at Wednesday's Press conference at Maidstone:—

"Last Tuesday the Home Office wanted to learn from the Board how soon we could regain access to Sheppey. Mr. Taylor advised us that if we took the safe course and relied on sluices for clearing the water from the Island, it would take roughly 21 days.

"We thought that was too long and so the engineer came to the conclusion that if access to the Island was to be gained within a reasonable time there was no alternative but to make further breaches in the river walls.

"A very grave risk was run when making such breaches because at the same time we had to consider steps to see that, come what may, they would be sealed by this Friday, otherwise we should be making the position worse.

"Unless we experience very serious weather during the next 48 hours, I think we will have succeeded in getting these breaches resealed and safe for the high tides expected between 14th and 18th."

24-HOUR WATCH ON SHEPPEY COAST DEFENCES

Emergency men ready for still higher tides

TOWN SHOULD BE SAFE IF—

ALONG the coast of Sheppey this week an all-out effort has been going on to prepare the sea defences for the shock of the spring tides which start this week-end and reach their peak on Monday.

Today (Friday) it is officially known that the defences, temporarily repaired by sandbagging, are now up to a standard described as being "no less than that reached before the flooding."

While this work has continued unceasingly, a snowstorm, driven by winds reaching 50 m.p.h., has hit the west coast. Slowly the storm centre has been moving eastwards, bringing with it dangerous northerly gales, sleet and snow. There is a possibility that it may have passed beyond these shores before the peak danger period of Monday.

That is the fervent hope of those whose responsibility has been to make Sheerness watertight. On Monday afternoon, at 2.51, will come the real testing time, when, according to Admiralty tide tables, the tide will reach a height of 18.5 feet: two feet in excess of that scheduled for the night of February 1.

WEEK-END: RAPID RISE

Tonight, or early tomorrow (Saturday) morning, the tides will have crept up one foot from the height of the previous day. In the early hours of Sunday afternoon it will have risen nearly another foot, making peak tides at a few minutes before two o'clock in the small hours of Monday morning (reaching 18.5), almost equal to the high tide in the afternoon.

Figures given apply to tides at normal strength. Temporary changes in meteorological conditions cannot be predicted, but their effect may, of course, be considerable. Generally speaking, the sea level is raised in the direction towards which the wind is blowing, and depressed in the direction from which it is blowing. Meteorological conditions in the North Sea can have a considerable effect upon the mean sea level, and this is particularly noticeable in the Thames Estuary and North Sea. In deep water, the height of the surge can raise the water level by as much as five feet.

BUT THE WORK GOES ON ...

With these and other considerations to be taken into account, civilian workers, together with hundreds of military service personnel, have continued their vital operations. From Blue Town to Queenborough Pier they have succeeded in weaving the breaches and restoring the original level of the sea wall.

At every other gap, also, the work has proceeded. Twenty thousand empty sandbags have been dropped by air and filled, while many thousands more have been supplied from naval sources.

SAND AND SNOW

On Sunday, while prayers were said in churches throughout the country for those engaged in defence work, men toiled in a blinding blizzard on Sheerness beach, helped by eager schoolboys, filling bags and loading them on to lorries.

So far as Sheerness is concerned, the defences have been temporarily restored by sandbagging; and provided there are no exceptional gales during the period of the spring tides, beginning on Friday, it is expected that the sea defences will be adequate to meet the tides. Naturally, further onshore gales could quite materially affect the situation.

A twenty-four-hour watch will be maintained on all areas in the urban district during this spring tide period, and squads of men will be standing by at night to be employed at any point where a weakness may appear in the defences.

The Surveyor (Mr. K. Scott) is arranging for a stock-pile of filled sandbags to be available at the two strategic points—West Minster and the Cheyney Rock area. These will be readily accessible for use should any emergency arise.

One squad of men will be based at West Minster, and will be constantly in communication with Mr. Scott at the control point at the Council Offices.

Apprentices are among some 500 to 600 men from Sheerness Dockyard

(Continued on page two)

THE IMPERMANENT WAY

NO trains are expected to run between Sheerness and the mainland for some days to come, but arrangements are being made for a bus service to help passengers from the Island to Sittingbourne station, as soon as conditions on the Ferry Bridge road permit.

Inspection trolleys have patrolled the permanent way between Sittingbourne and Queenborough, and trains carrying men and materials for repair work will follow today (Friday), filling in gaps and re-laying lines, so that eventually they can regain contact with Sheerness station.

"HANDS OFF SANDBAGS"

—COUNCIL WARNING

REPORTS of thefts from emergency sandbag piles, placed along the sea wall for use in the event of further crisis during the spring tide period, were heard at an emergency meeting of Sheerness Urban District Council on Wednesday.

The following statement was issued: "Sandbags have been stolen from the Neptune Terrace area. These are placed at points along the sea wall for use in the event of emergency, and under no circumstances are they to be taken away by members of the general public for their own use."

WATER FROM MAINS IN A FEW DAYS?

THE following statement on water supplies has been issued by the Sheerness Urban District Council:—

Boreholes; Water has been pumped away to get rid of salt contamination. Chemical analyses are improving in quality every day, and it is hoped that it may be possible to restore normal supplies in the mains within the next few days. This depends entirely on the results of bacteriological analyses of the water, which are being carried out daily.

ON OTHER PAGES

Latest news on the floods, together with more graphic stories of the people's ordeal, their gradual return to normal life with the help of hundreds of volunteers, appears on pages 2, 3, 4, 5, 7 and 8. More exclusive pictures appear on pages 7 and 8.

PROBABLE COST OF REPAIRS BETWEEN £10 & £15 MILLION

Further damage may be caused, River Board Clerk tells Press

THE cost of repairing the shattered Kent sea and river walls may be between £10 and £15 million, and, despite the efforts of the Kent River Board to close all breaches, further flooding can be expected in the Isle of Sheppey between Saturday and next Wednesday.

This news was given by Mr. J. I. Taylor, deputy engineer to the Kent River Board, at a Press conference at Maidstone on Tuesday. Mr. Taylor has been in charge since the start of the emergency because the chief engineer is ill.

His words were: "It is inevitable that a great deal of water will enter where we have not been able to seal the breaches. This applies particularly to parts of Sheppey and the northern sea wall between Receivers and Birchington . . .

"But Sheerness should be safe. If, however, there is a repetition of the gales which drove the last high tide across and through the sea walls, the flooding may be even more serious than it was two weeks ago."

CHAIRMAN'S STATEMENT

The chairman of the Board, Mr. G. J. Gully, in a statement on the damage, said there were originally over 3000 breaches in the sea and river walls between Woolwich and Deal. But what was possibly more serious was the fact that between those breaches, the walls that remain standing have, generally speaking, been very seriously scoured on the land side, and thereby dangerously weakened.

"Up to Monday noon approximately 300 breaches have been temporarily sealed and the extent of the area remaining inundated has been very greatly reduced, but a large amount of remedial work still remains.

(Continued on page two)

The only road leading to Littlebrook Power Station at Dartford was washed away. Here the Royal Engineers from Chatham with outboard motor boats run a ferry service for the staff.

These three men are not waiting for a bus. They are negotiating the flood waters at Erith on crude rafts made from broken doors.

Mr Harold Jordan of Whitstable is rescued from his bedroom window. Under his arm he carries a most treasured possession.

There was no football in this stadium for some time. The Gravesend and Northfleet ground looking more like a boating lake.

A desolate scene on the front at Margate after the floods had receded.

Twenty people were trapped overnight on this coach between Sittingbourne and Sheerness and had to be rescued by an amphibious vehicle from Faversham which made six recovery trips.

The canyon at Beltinge where 100,000 tons of soil subsided. A gas board employee peers over the edge of the cliff in an attempt to find the broken mains

The frigate HMS Berkeley Castle was in dry dock at Sheerness for temporary repair. During the gale it was turned on its side.

A young and smiling Queen gives encouragement to flood victims at Erith when she toured the stricken areas on the Thames Estuary. As yet uncrowned, her Coronation took place four months later on a cold and wet day in June, 1953.

New defences for Kent

THE people of Kent, more aware than ever of the dangers facing them from the inundation of the sea, demanded immediate action in repairing, strengthening and extending the inadequate defences. A committee appointed by the Government suggested, somewhat alarmingly, that there could be an increase in the levels reached by the 1953 tidal surge and such occurrences could be more frequent. The Waverley Committee advocated the installation of a flood warning system to prevent loss of life. The problem was tackled immediately and engineers worked at a tremendous speed, although it was to be many years before all the new defences were completed. The Erith sea wall, forming part of the South Bank of The Thames and protecting industrial areas, was heightened - in some places by four feet above the 1953 tide level. The Queensborough Wall on the Isle of Sheppey, also protecting a built-up area, was raised four feet above the highest level reached in 1953. At Sheerness, sea-drained shingle was pumped ashore to help conserve the beach. It was placed on the foreshore over a length of 875 yards.

The Woolwich and the Grain sea walls were also heightened and reinforced; the Graveney wall along the Medway Estuary and the Seasalter sea walls were equipped with concrete parapets. At Whitstable the council raised the new wall by a further three feet and storm surge barriers were inserted. The northern sea wall between Reculver and Birchington was strengthened by interlocking concrete blocks, and a second line of defence was constructed along the railway behind the wall.

In London - which had teetered on the brink of a massive disaster - the Great Flood Barrier, costing more than £100 million, was constructed at Woolwich. It is a fact that the boroughs of Hammersmith, Wandsworth, Lambeth, Tower Hamlets, Greenwich and Westminster lie below the maximum level reached by the 1953 tides. On that occasion water actually lapped the top of the parapet along the Victoria and Chelsea embankments. The defences were overtopped by a few inches at Greenwich and London Bridge.

The flood barrier was desperately urgent for there had always been the possibility that meteorological and tidal conditions could combine to produce a surge more disastrous than 1703, 1897 or 1953. And, without the defensive barrier, low-lying London, with its vast underground system, could drown completely.

1st February, 1954 and the 432 inhabitants of the village of Eastling, near Faversham have been cut off from the outside world for more than two days. Snow-ploughs made some progress but men from Faversham were the first to reach the snow-bound village after digging their way through for several hours.

Hemmed in by ice

SOME of the most severe weather conditions in East Kent since 1940 froze the River Stour for many miles, killed thousands of fish and brought road and river traffic to a standstill in the first week of February, 1954. The Esso tanker, Stourgate, was completely surrounded by thick ice and had to delay her journey to the plant. Because of this, supplies at the oil depot diminished and paraffin had to be brought to Sandwich from London.

Thousands of dead fish were seen in the river. They had apparently gone through the Stonar Cut and into the colder waters where they perished. Pegwell Bay was also frozen and seagulls spent many hours pecking holes in the ice in an attempt to get through to the water.

The Sarre to Ramsgate road was impassable and snow-ploughs worked throughout the night. Villagers in Eastling, Huckling, Lynsted, Stowting and Hastingleigh were cut off for three days. On the Medway, ice up to three feet thick covered the river for more than 20 miles.

Mount Ephraim post mill, Ash, which was destroyed in the storm of 1955. See page 87.

The notice affixed to the tree by Keston Ponds was quite clear: "The public are warned that these ponds are deep and dangerous. Bathers and skaters venture at their own risk". Those who took the risk on Sunday 1st February, 1954 — and there were many of them — were quite safe. The ice was many inches thick and the temperature was below freezing for the ninth consecutive day. In fact the Arctic conditions caused two Bromley schools to be closed so hundreds of children had a further opportunity to take themselves and their skates to Keston Ponds.

Sea Defences Sternly Tested

A gale which raged across East Kent for three days in October 1955 destroyed the oldest post mill in the county, and possibly in England. The Mount Ephraim windmill at Ash, near Sandwich, which was built in 1735, was hurled to the ground and smashed beyond repair by hurricane-force winds that sternly tested the gigantic sea defences built after the 1953 floods.

Hundreds of police, firemen and coastguards, alerted by an amber flood warning flashed from police headquarters at Maidstone, remained on duty throughout the night at danger points along the North Kent shore watching the sea batter the concrete and steel barriers. High tide in the early hours of Saturday morning, 22nd October was the time of crisis. From Sheppey to Thanet and down the east coast, buildings were damaged and promenades piled high with shingle, seaweed and driftwood.

But the new sea defences held. There was no flooding at any point.

The Trinity House tender Vestal and three of her crew at the scene of the South Goodwin disaster. Above the water is all that remains of the lightship.

Goodwin Lightship Tragedy

1 November 1954

A series of intense depressions which moved northwards off Iceland resulted in a prolonged spell of violent gales during the five days between 26th and 30th November, 1954. The Kent coastal resorts between Ramsgate and Dungenness were attacked by strong gusts but the most tragic incident was the loss of the South Goodwin Lightship which broke her moorings on the eastern side of the sands, where she capsized drowning all seven of her crew. Three lifeboats, from Walmer, Dover and Ramsgate rushed to her aid along with the Trinity House tenders Vestal and Patricia, HMS Romola and a team of naval divers. The crew were all gone but miraculously there was one survivor —Ronald Murton, a Ministry of Agriculture scientist, who was on the ship engaged in bird watching. As the South Goodwin lay on her side part buried by sand Mr Murton was seen by a helicopter clinging on to the wreck.

When the storm abated a memorial service was held at sea on December 3 at which the Ramsgate and Walmer lifeboats tied up alongside each other close to the wreck while wreaths were cast upon the water.

Several other ships were wrecked off the Kent coast during this storm which broke new records. At Brawdy in West Wales the gusts reached at strength of 185 kph (115 miles an hour), a record for the whole of Britain for November.

The Ramsgate and Walmer Lifeboats are tied to each other while a memorial service is held at sea for the seven crew members of the South Goodwin who died at sea during the gale of November 28, 1954.

Heavy snow on 15th January, 1955 followed by a rapid thaw, then rain, brought new flooding to Canterbury, Maidstone and Tonbridge. In Maidstone, Royal Engineers from the Invicta Barracks helped to clear away the snow but they were helpless the next day, as the river level rose almost to the top of the bridge across the Medway. Thirty years later the photograph shows them helping out again.

Maidstone's Floodmarker

IN 1955 the old floodmarker by the brewery in Maidstone received its final entry. It bore witness to a number of inundations but clearly showed that the greatest of them all took place in the years 1814 and 1900.

During the arctic-like month of January 1814, all over England rivers became encrusted with ice which became solid enough to bear the weight of a horse and cart. A Great Frost Fair was held on the Thames where shops and booths were erected and thousands of people flocked to see such sights as sheep being roasted on the ice and printers plying their presses.

The Medway, too, was held fast in ice. Thick snow had fallen mid-month but in early February began to melt and the river's frozen surface started to break up sending massive ice floes downstream. These became entrapped by the narrow spans of the Great Bridge and, acting like the walls of a dam, raised the river level to unprecedented heights.

RAF to the Rescue

DURING the second world war no-one was allowed to drive or walk past the RAF fighter station at Biggin Hill for security reasons. In mid-February, 1956 no-one could walk or drive along the famous stretch of road. It was blocked by snow-drifts almost six feet high which had been swept by severe and bitter winds from the airfield and were causing serious traffic problems. The RAF provided the solution. They opened the road across the airfield and through their camp to regular traffic, while snow-ploughs and blowers were busy on the other section.

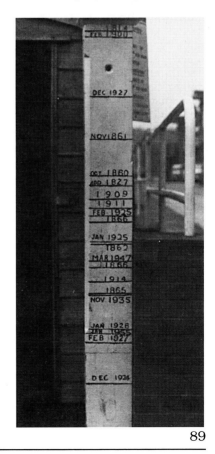

August Bank Holiday, 1956 and the white carpet of ice which lay across the road in Tunbridge Wells.

Ice in August. The front page of the The Kent and Sussex Courier.

Fantasy on an August Day

August Monday, 1956

THE scene in Tunbridge Wells on August Bank Holiday Monday in 1956 was one of pure fantasy. A freak storm unleashed so many hailstones they formed a moving icy mass which, an eye witness said, looked like "rice pudding on an unimaginable scale spreading through the town".

It was in the middle of the morning on Monday 6th August that the storm began. Thunder and lightning were followed by heavy rain which soon turned into hail. At first the hailstones were small but just before mid-day they bombarded down from the sky as big as cherries, smashing windows and skylights and tearing shop blinds to shreds. The storm was localised. While it raged in Tunbridge Wells and to a lesser extent in Tonbridge and Southborough, villages a few miles away had fine bank holiday weather.

The scene in the centre of Tunbridge Wells was astounding. Everywhere the hailstones made a white carpet and water pouring off the Common and down the High Street and the Frant Road swept the hail into great drifts by the Pantiles traffic lights. As soon as the hail stopped, local residents and passers-by left cover, rolled up their trouser legs and tried to clear the blocked drains. As they worked, a single deck bus came down the Frant Road and the driver signalled that he was going to drive straight through. The bus entered the water in a great wave but hailstones piled up against it shoulder high. It was stranded there for three hours.

Two young people in particular will remember this day of meteorological madness. Mr R Dawes and Miss C.D. Saunders, both of Tunbridge Wells, were due to be married at St James Church. Just before the service started the building was struck by lightning and the organ was flooded. The ceremony went ahead without the music.

There were other scenes of chaos. Shop ceilings collapsed in the High Street and there was extensive damage at Weekes and Dusts. In Tonbridge, a Buick car standing at the back of Tonbridge Motor Service garage was almost completely submerged by flood water. Inside the car, taking refuge from the storm, was the owner's wife, Mrs Penn and her two small girls. As the water rose Mrs Penn began to get worried. She sounded the horn and the three were carried to safety. Outside, the hailstones were piled high in the road and more than 100 lorry loads were carried away.

A spectacular thunderstorm over North Kent on July 18, 1956 flooded many roads and completely paralysed traffic. At Sutton at Hone, near Dartford, Mr John Martindale became marooned. While getting out of his car a rush of water with brick rubble from a nearby farm knocked him over and he broke both of his legs. The piled up straw in front of his car shows how high the water rose.

Trains Crash at Lewisham in the Fog

4th December, 1957

FIVE years after the "smog" of 1952 South London experienced another "pea-souper" and another disaster. On 4th December, 1957 two trains crashed at Lewisham in thick fog under a bridge which then collapsed onto the wrecked coaches. Ninety two passengers died and 200 were injured. Many of them came from Kent.

The tragedy occurred when a fast steam train from Cannon Street to Ramsgate ran into the back of an electric locomotive standing in Lewisham station. It is believed that, in the gloom, the driver missed three warning lights.

The trains were packed with City workers and Christmas shoppers. Most of the victims were pinned down in the tangle of twisted metal. Ambulancemen stationed only 200 yards away at Lewisham Hospital were later joined by Royal Engineers in digging for survivors.

On impact one of the carriages reared up, smashing bridge supports, moments before a third train approached the broken bridge. The driver had slowed down because of the poor visibility and stopped his cab just a few feet short of the edge.

Many of those killed and injured came from Tonbridge, Tunbridge Wells, Ashford and the Thanet towns. Memorial services were held throughout Kent and a fund was opened for victims and for the "wonderful folk of Lewisham who rendered aid". The chairman of Kent County Council, Sir William Nottidge said: "We in Kent owe a great deal of gratitude to the rescuers, the heroic men and women who worked so hard in such harrowing conditions".

There is little doubt that the cause of the crash was radiation fog, formed when the sky was clear of cloud, the wind light and there was an anticyclone nearby. One man from Tonbridge who was on the train said the fog was appalling when it left Cannon Street. "I managed to crawl out of the wreckage at 7.30 pm and made my way to a newsagent's shop where I persuaded a Sevenoaks taxi to come and pick me up." The taxi arrived at about 10pm, no mean feat, for the visibility was about five yards at best.

Crayford-in-the-floods on the evening of 5th September, 1958 after a storm of tropical intensity had brought traffic to a halt.

When the Chestnut Fell

5th September, 1958

"COME and see this", the young weather-watcher shouted out to his parents and soon they joined all their neighbours in the street to gaze in awe, looking skywards towards the south-west from Chislehurst. Dozens of people stood looking at a celestial firework display likened to the flames of an artillery barrage from a thousand armies. Thunderless at first, then gradually becoming an unceasing cannonade, the storm was soon to begin.

An hour earlier, unbeknown to the residents of West Kent, a violent storm had developed to the south of Horsham in Sussex. Hailstones the size of tennis balls had smashed windows, lacerated and bruised people, damaged aircraft and split tree bark. Indeed, these were the largest hailstones ever to fall in the British Isles. Through the chaos a tornado had cut a swathe of destruction. This self-perpetuating travelling thunderstorm, guided by upper winds, now headed for Kent and unleashed a deluge over Knockholt that, at the time, was the second heaviest two hour rainfall this country had ever experienced, a staggering 5.14 inches (131 mm), two months' supply.

The County Fire Brigade received 1,345 storm related calls. Potentially the most dangerous incident was when two enormous tanks of crude oil were set ablaze by lightning at BP's Isle of Grain refinery. After some hours the fire was contained and disaster avoided.

For Mrs Edith Stone, aged 72, the evening became a life and death struggle when flood water poured into her ground floor flat off the Fawkham Road in Longfield. Desperately she tried to leave; in water up to her armpits she finally forced the door open and reached a neighbour's house, where she collapsed exhausted and plastered in mud.

As Mrs Stone was fighting for her life, motorists were stranded and animals drowned. Hundreds of telephone and power lines were severed and trees uprooted. At Farningham the world famous giant horse-chestnut tree, the second largest in England and a sapling at the time of the Great Plague and Fire of London was felled by a combination of fiercesome winds and undermining caused by a raging torrent from the swollen River Darent.

Floods and landslides disrupted trains, including those between Mottingham and Dartford, and Sevenoaks and Tonbridge where hundreds of tons of soil and rock were brought down. It was many days before the branch line from Dunton Green to Westerham re-opened. A train from Victoria with pilgrims to Lourdes came to a halt at Eynsford for six hours; passengers were given tea and light refreshments by the local rector's wife.

The deluge washed crops away. At Horton Kirby five acres of hops were ruined. Waves of mud, 18 inches deep, covered roads at Southfleet.

Gravesend High Street became a river and in the Woodlands Park and Valley Drive areas, flooding was chest deep; even pianos floated in the debris-laden waters. At Shortlands, near Bromley, a resident described the events: "During 54 years here at Meadow Road I have never witnessed such scenes. Filthy oil-laden water poured over the banks of the Ravensbourne and swelled into a vast lake across the lower recreation ground. What was the bowling green became a sea of squelchy mud". At Clockhouse Station floodwaters from the Chaffinch Brook raced up the tracks from one direction, only to be met by a surge of water coming in the opposite direction from Elmers End. Water reached platform level.

At Ruxley Manor School, between Mottingham and Chislehurst, rain poured off a sloping field and the wall adjoining the playground, acting like a dam, collapsed, showering tons of earth and bricks onto the playground. The rain, amounting to over 300 tons per acre, was also responsible for a massive subsidence outside the home of Mr Hadlow in Betsham. A crater 50 feet deep and 60 feet wide, believed to be a former dene hole, opened up. In Swanscombe a man fell 20 feet when a footpath caved in near a disused chalkpit. He was lucky to escape from the crumbling chasm after spending some time scrambling up its sides.

Many of Kent's famous buildings were damaged, including Hever Castle and Westerham's Quebec House, the boyhood home of General Wolfe. At Beckenham three houses had to be entirely demolished, they were so badly flooded. In a bizarre incident at Swanscombe a 52-foot high flag pole was hit by lightning cutting a 14-foot section out of the middle, thereby plunging the top onto the lower part so that it looked as before, only shorter! In all, 12 houses were struck by the incessant lightning with Bromley and Sidcup suffering the most "hits".

The storm was thought by many to be the worst of the century; hydrologists calculated that the return period for such an event was as many as 160 years. Few people would have believed that an even greater fall of rain was to create havoc in the same area just 10 years later.

1959: A hot and dry summer was accompanied, in August, by violent storms. Much of the South of England, including Kent, was lashed by torrential rain on 10th August followed by another deluge on 21st, when three quarters of an inch fell in one hour in London. In the City floods caused considerable chaos.

The Cloister
FIREPLACE
produced by
STOOKE & SPARKS
(Gravesend) Ltd.
QUEEN STREET

CHIESMANS
at GRAVESEND, Ltd. Tel. 251
REMOVALS : STORAGE : SHIPPING

GRAVESEND & DARTFORD REPORTER

NORTHFLEET REPORTER, NORTH
KENT & SOUTH ESSEX ADVERTISER

Woodford & Co
WINES & SPIRITS
Agents for
TRUMAN'S
BEERS
PARROCK ST.,
GRAVESEND
Telephone: 394.

TELEVISION—
Bush, Marconi, H.M.V., Cossor, Pye,
STORES,
RAINBOW GRAVESEND

No. 5,351. | REGISTERED AT THE GENERAL POST OFFICE AS A NEWSPAPER | SATURDAY, SEPTEMBER 13, 1958. | POST FREE 7s 1d PER QUARTER IN ADVANCE | ESTABLISHED 1858 | 4d.

THE MOST SEVERE THUNDERSTORM WITHIN LIVING MEMORY LASHES NORTH KENT FOR TWO HOURS

Severe floods follow torrential rain, thunder and hail

A TWO-HOUR thunderstorm that broke with tropical intensity over North Kent and parts of Sussex, Surrey and Essex on Friday evening did hundreds of thousands of pounds worth of damage to property and crops, disrupted rail, road and ferry services, and seriously flooded wide areas of town and country.

The storm, accompanied by almost continuous lightning and thunder, brought with it one of the heaviest hailstorms for years. At places it was reported that they were as big as walnuts.

The lightning was so incessant that, at times, it looked just like a heavy barrage of anti-aircraft guns.

When the hail was at its height, the roads were literally white with the stones as they crashed down. They made an alarming crash and rattle of sound as they pelted into windows and on to roofs.

Traffic was slowed and finally brought to a standstill. Many motorists abandoned their vehicles.

In Gravesend, 3.58 inches of rain was measured. Within a short time the torrential rain was overflowing the drainage system and roads began to go under water to a depth of several inches.

As the downpour continued the water rose to several feet in depth.

Gravesend firemen were reinforced and were kept busy all through the night and for the following days pumping out flooded cellars and shops.

Priority on Friday night was given to premises where food was stored.

Dene hole under the sun-lounge

Holes appeared in the ground at several spots. Dene holes were uncovered. One of them was under the sun-lounge of the home of Mr. and Mrs. E. F. Roberts, at 12, Singlewell-road, Gravesend.

A part of the back lawn disappeared down a 14-feet-deep

cavity that ran under the back of the premises, which were left overlapping the edge of the hole.

Half-way down it, and leading off, was another tunnel, believed to be a dene hole going many feet deep into the earth.

"This all appeared in the night," Mr. Roberts, an expert dahlia grower, told the "Reporter."

One of the worst hit parts of Gravesend was in the Valley-drive area where upwards of a dozen houses were flooded to a depth of several feet.

Not long after the storm hit the town, reports were coming in of serious flooding and damage.

Manhole covers were blown off and sewerage was forced up through the cavity as the main drainage system became overloaded and unable to cope with the deluge.

RIVER FLEET IS 'REBORN'

IN the rural areas matters were extremely grim.

Trees crashed down blocking roads. Water, driven by the high wind, swirled off the fields into the roads and through houses, some of which were flooded and mud-covered to the depth of nearly a foot.

Carpets and furniture were ruined.

Large areas of cut corn were devastated and stocks of corn were swept away to distances of up to a mile, to be left floating in huge lakes that had formed in the lower lying areas of the fields.

One of the worst spots was at Southfleet, where residents think that the one-time River Fleet was brought back to life.

The edge of the dene hole which appeared beneath the sun-lounge of a house in Singlewell-road, Gravesend.

Listen to the alarming experience of Mrs. Elsie M. Cripps who lives at "The Croft," Red Street.

All the electricity in the district had failed, and Mrs. Croft was sitting in her front room in the dark.

She was alone, her husband having gone off on night work at Kent Works, Stone. Her son was out.

"I was sitting there in the dark and scared out of my wits when suddenly I heard a noise like a train coming," she said. "Then I saw the water rushing off the field and across the road right in front of my bungalow. Within minutes it was over the front garden and in the house.

"Mud came in with it and there was nothing I could do about it. Boxes of potatoes were being carried off the fields half-a-mile away and were being dumped in the road.

"The corner of Red Street was soon blocked with mud, and parts of the roadway came up. I have been here since February and we had just got things nicely settled ... now look."

After the storm had subsided, Mrs. Cripps' belongings were a wreck.

So was part of the back garden which was covered up to several inches with thick, glutinous mud. The smell was most unpleasant.

Shock for young married couple

Many residents in the Red Street area are angry with the Parish Council. They claim that every time it rains with any intensity there is flooding there.

Said one: "We have complained several times to the local Council, but they seem to do just nothing about it. If this is not a case for main drainage we don't know what it is. It's time they did away with these old-fashioned cesspools and brought the village up-to-date with the times."

Bitterly surveying their ruined property was a young married couple, Mr. and Mrs.

K. C. Bigg. They said that in the four-and-a-half months they have been living in their new bungalow at Red Street the road outside their home has been flooded every time it rained. They have only got out by using the next door neighbour's property.

At the time of the storm they were on a touring holiday in France, and came back over the week-end to find their newly-furnished home in a shocking state.

They were high in their praise for the local police constable and neighbours who had got into the house and cleared out the worst of the mud and slime.

On Monday, three days after, the only way to get to the house was by wading on planks over several inches of thick mud.

Demand for Council action

"We really think it is time our Council took action to see this sort of thing does not happen again," said Mr. Bigg. "We are always troubled with flooded roads at this spot after any sort of heavy rain. I have written to the Council twice on the subject and have had replies but no action."

Residents, armed with torches, went to the assistance of motorists stranded near "The Ship," Southfleet, where the cross roads were flooded to a depth of several feet.

The motorists had been re-directed along the Southfleet route as other roads rapidly became impassable.

"It was a nightmare," one said. "There we were trying to work with the aid of torches—and the rain and hail lashing down all the time. The lightning was intense and many people, especially the elderly living on their own, were scared stiff. And they had every right to be."

In the "local" business went on with the aid of candles. Water swirled past the door and many gardens were flooded.

A barn, containing onions, burst, and the vegetables floated on the flood waters all over the fields.

Another resident claimed that he saw the old river come to life.

"Suddenly the old path of the river filled," he said.

"Water gushed along making a fearful noise and carrying all sorts of stuff before it. It bore down on its old track until it came to a hillside where it was diverted, taking a lot of the banking with it."

Other residents, with houses on higher land, came to the assistance of those washed out and gave them shelter for the night.

For Southfleet it was certainly a night to remember.

WEEK-END MEAT DAMAGED

THE Perry Street, Northfleet, district always suffers in heavy rainfall. Cellars beneath shops were flooded and cases of goods and foodstuffs bobbed about in the flood waters.

A number of shops in the area were flooded. Mr. R. F. King's butchers shop had Saturday morning meat supplies damaged when water seeped into refrigeration plant.

Several refrigerators were put out of action.

Glebe-road and Victoria-road residents had to contend with flooded rooms. Here, a petition was circulated and signed by scores of householders protesting against the inadequate drainage. The letter will be sent to the Mayor of Gravesend, the Borough Surveyor and health authorities.

Barrels of beer were afloat beneath the Fleet Tavern at Waterdales.

Fire appliances went to Taunton-road and Burch-road, Northfleet, to pump water from houses.

lives in the fields, and a haystack was reported to have been afloat.

Along Watling-street there were several cases of flooding. Mud and gravel nearly a foot deep in places, covered a 30-yard stretch near the Merrie-chest café.

Further towards London scores of cars were left abandoned at the roadside and their owners and passengers sought shelter when the road commenced to flood.

An 84-years-old widow living alone in Hollands-close, Shorne, had a frightening experience. Mrs. Sandford, cut off by the heavy downpour, heard the rain dislodging bricks from her chimney.

Firemen get three hundred calls for assistance

AS water cascaded down Gravesend High-street the Gravesend-Tilbury passenger ferry went out of service.

There were immense pools of water outside the "Three Daws" at the bottom of High-street and persons leaving the Town Pier had to be carried off by workmen who were dressed for the job.

The vehicle ferry kept running and took on foot passengers. Said Captain Albert Bevan: "I have been on the service for 39 years and I have never experienced anything like this before. At times it was quite terrifying."

At the height of the storm the Gravesend fire service was receiving calls for assistance at the rate of over one a minute. In all over 300 calls were taken during the night.

Firemen worked like Trojans to pump out flooded dwellings and help stricken householders.

On top of that they had to send a crew to the Isle of Grain where fire had broken out at the refinery. Two storage tanks burst into flames after being struck by lightning. One burned for several hours.

The 18ft. deep cellar at the Fisherman's Arms, West-street, Gravesend, overflowed and water in the bars was two feet deep. Customers were standing barefoot in the bar.

● TURN TO PAGE 16

Gravesend main road flooded

NEW-ROAD, Gravesend, was flooded and bus passengers squatted on tables in the London Transport waiting room before wading to the stops.

Gravesend Central station was closed to rail passengers and scores of people waded to the main road, hoping to catch Green Line coaches.

At Hammonds' Corner, Singlewell-road, water on the road surface washed into shop cellars. Occupiers rang the police and bus garages to ask for traffic to be diverted through Mead-road.

There were crazy scenes on the Wrotham-road past the Tollgate. Homegoing motorists met a wall of mud which had slumped from banks on the roadside.

Farmland at Northumberland Bottom was still like a lake this week. Also in the Istead Rise area, cattle were swimming for their

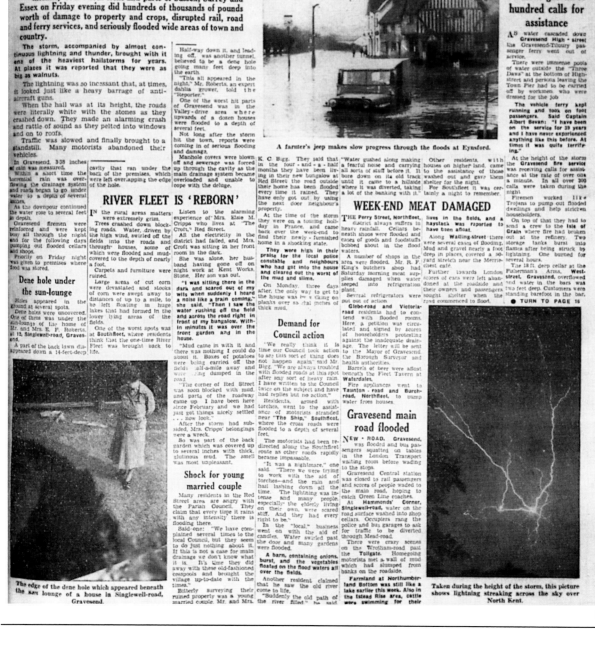

A farmer's jeep makes slow progress through the floods at Eynsford.

Taken during the height of the storm, this picture shows lightning streaking across the sky over North Kent.

Tony Durrant of Faraday Avenue, Sidcup is suitably attired to make a telephone call for assistance, as the flood waters continue to rise.

The scene at Dover Hill on 23rd January, 1958 as cars and trucks, immobilised by the slippery roads, queued up to be pushed.

To Monte Carlo via Dover Hill

24th January, 1958

KENT greeted the Monte Carlo competitors on Wednesday night, 24th January, 1958 with a foretaste of the alpine conditions that drivers had hoped to escape until reaching the French mountains.

The 85 drivers began their journey in Glasgow, drove through falling snow in Scotland and England and reached East Kent only to find conditions appalling. Many chose to take the A2 through Sittingbourne, Faversham and Canterbury but the others tackled Dover Hill where a huge crowd gathered in arctic conditions to see the competitors slide, sometimes sideways, up the notorious hill.

Unbelievable scenes greeted those who dared to venture out the following day. The rally drivers had gone but hundreds of abandoned cars were strewn across the roads between Folkestone, Dover and Deal. Villages were cut off and thousands were forced to walk to work. At Capel there was no sign of any cars - they were totally buried under mountainous snow-drifts.

The most tragic story concerned a little girl who was seriously ill in Dover Isolation Hospital and needed immediate treatment. A police car with a surgeon and specialist somehow battled its way through the drifts to Dover but the child had died.

Miners from Tilmanstone Colliery left their shift at 6am on Thursday morning and reached their homes in Dover five hours later. In these conditions even snow-ploughs were stuck in the East Kent drifts.

Fire and Floods

TROOPS had to be drafted in to help fight grass and woodland fires during the burning hot summer of 1959. During the five months from June to mid-October, Kent Fire Brigade received so many calls for assistance in the countryside that crews had to be redirected by radio from one area to another.

During the hot spell, on 29th July, a thunderstorm caused flash flooding in many areas of North Kent. John and Madelene Rahtz found the perfect way of getting home - a canoe trip down Hurst Road, Sidcup.

November, 1960 and it's lovely weather for duckboards in Maidstone !

Fairfield is a village of marshland and scattered farms, two miles south of Appledore. The church of St Thomas of Canterbury is normally surrounded by dykes and sheep but in November, 1960 it stood alone in a great expanse of water.

Vast Lake to the Sea

November 1960

JOHN Wells, MP for Maidstone, supported the motion in the House of Commons for the launch of a national disaster fund in the wake of the November floods of 1960 which swamped many low-lying valleys in England and Wales. Compared to the West Country, where lives were lost, Kent fared lightly but after a week of monsoon-type rain, most rivers in the county burst their banks, with all the accompanying chaos and misery.

In Maidstone, water poured out of the Medway and down the High Street. Ducks were swimming in Palace Gardens and office girls were carried to work by gallant workmen in gum boots. The Medway continued to rise and Kent River Board recommended the evacuation of homes, shops and offices in vulnerable parts of the town.

The Rother Valley, from Newenden to Rye, resembled one vast lake. Parts of Canterbury were under water and the corporation donkeys were moved out of the town gardens. The move was a wise one. Within hours the grounds were totally submerged. Many Kent villages were badly flooded and bridges damaged. Smarden, Benenden, Wateringbury, Harrietsham and Hunton were the worst affected and many homes were evacuated. To the people in Chislet, Grove Ferry, Wickhambreaux, Ash-next-Sandwich, Harbledown, Godmersham and Chartham it was the same dismal story.

In the villages around Tonbridge, where the floods were described yet again as "the worst in living memory", East Peckham and Paddock Wood were completely waterlogged and in Yalding, food supplies were delivered by the vicar in an amphibious vehicle. Penshurst village, on the Eden, was marooned but hundreds of sheep were rescued in time to save them from drowning.

For Kent Fire Brigade the November floods provided the largest pumping operation since February 1953. The first calls came on 31st October and rapidly increased. At the height of the emergency, on 4th November, hundreds of firemen, units of the AFS and volunteers battled against rising floods and the BBC announced that 10,000 acres of land in the Medway Valley were under water.

Practically every part of the county was on a state of emergency and one of the biggest tasks for the Fire Brigade was to protect and restore essential services, fresh water supplies and communication. Every cloud has a silver lining, even for the embattled fire service. The 5th November fell right in the middle of the emergency; Guy Fawkes night in Kent was a damp squib and hardly any calls were received to bonfires out of control.

The year 1960 was a wet one for Kent. In August the Medway had misbehaved again and the little hamlet of Laddingford, near Yalding was cut off. At Hawley, near Dartford, torrents of rain washed tons of mud and onions from a field into homes. There was some good news, however, for the Medway towns, especially Rochester, Strood and Chatham. That week, work began on the massive £2 million A2 bridge spanning one of the widest parts of the river between Cuxton and Borstal.

5th November, 1960. The Reverend G.T. Gray, vicar of St Peter's and St Paul's Church, Yalding sailed around his flooded village in a locally owned Dukw, giving what assistance he could to distressed parishoners.

The Rother Valley, upstream from Newenden in November, 1960 following a week of torrential rain and 90mph gales. It was reported that the River Rother right down to Rye resembled a huge lake. This aerial photograph gives ample proof.

For two days in December, 1962 normal life was completely disrupted in parts of Kent and London by another heavy fog (or "smog"). In the capital alone, the number of deaths attributed to the conditions rose to more than 30. Many Kentish people working in London made use of the special mask which purifies the air before intake into the lungs.

14th November, 1961. The fishing boat Rose Marie was picked up by waves and dumped outside the Regent Cinema in Deal by a gale which lashed the Kent coast. Lifeboats had a busy time; on one occasion the Walmer Lifeboat was unable to land at Deal and had to proceed to dock in Dover. The Margate boat was trapped in its station when heavy seas bent the iron bars that secure the doors. The advertised film at the Regent Cinema was most appropriate.

Severe frosts occurred in the early part of December and just before Christmas, 1962. It was, of course, the prelude to one of the coldest winters of the century. At Goudhurst there were 100 days of frost. This spectacular picture was taken at Dartford Heath.

Visions of Antarctica

The winter of 1962-3

IT was a calm, grey, bitter afternoon with an earlier sharp frost still coating everything in an icy mantle. Just after three o'clock a few snow-flakes floated harmlessly to earth - advance guards of a far more potent force to follow. Within a few hours all Kent was thickly covered and, as the light faded on this Boxing Day 1962, lawns and village greens would not be visible again until early March.

The snow fell thickly throughout the night and the following day. Transport was brought to a halt with a 10 inch cover in the St Mary Cray area. No wind disturbed the tumbling flakes and it was a strangely muffled world. All trace of kerbs and roadways, paths and verges had gone. Only the bravest of motorists negotiated the Sidcup by-pass, some with snow-chains attached to the wheels of their beleaguered vehicles.

However, a worse foe was to strike. Gathering energy in the warmer waters off Cornwall, a deepening depression was heading towards southern England. It struck during the evening of Saturday 29th. Masses of fine crystalline snow fell and, driven by a severe gale, huge drifts formed, in places up to 15 feet deep. County-wide, a fleet of 300 snow-ploughs was mobilised but the task ahead was gigantic. At Bluebell Hill, between Maidstone and the Medway towns, it became an arctic nightmare for the mile-long queues of stranded motorists. There were similar scenes between Harrietsham and Charing and on Wrotham Hill.

By Sunday morning, Kent was almost at a standstill. Trains were abandoned at Faversham, Sellinge, Tonbridge and Shepherdswell, Orpington and Sevenoaks. At one point it was impossible to reach London by road. Twenty villages and hamlets were entirely isolated including Ash, Meopham, Adisham and Anvil Green near Canterbury and Leysdown on Thanet. In just a few days snow clearance alone had cost £200,000.

The conditions made for some improvisation and a horse and toboggan were used to carry milk and supplies to householders at Istead Rise, Northfleet. A woman in Maude Road, Hextable, going into early labour, found her way to hospital blocked by snow. Ambulances from Bromley and Farningham were also beaten by the elements. Eventually, Dartford police co-ordinated a rescue bid commandeering a snow-plough to dig a way through. Mrs Cockhead arrived at Westhill Hospital just a few hours before her baby was delivered.

After every snow-fall Kent awaits the thaw and there were signs in early January that milder air would gradually bring an end to the bitterly cold conditions.

As the mercury crept above freezing point new hazards of fog and rain falling on still-icy ground made for some perilous driving conditions. Optimism soon faded, however, as a renewed surge of cold easterlies sent fuel bills soaring, brought power cuts to homes and factories, and lay-offs to the building industry.

By the end of January, scenes along the Kentish coast indicated that this was no ordinary cold spell. At Herne Bay the frozen waters stretched two and a half miles out to sea, a sight never-to-be-forgotten by those who witnessed it. Margate Pier was surrounded by pancake ice and tugs battled against ice floes on the Medway at Chatham. Towards the middle of February, ice extended along the North Kent coast for seven miles, gently rising and falling with the tide. Ice on Reculver's beach lay several feet thick and floes rounded the North Foreland littered the harbours at Broadstairs and Ramsgate, the water having the appearance of a thick, hard porridge. Boats were held fast in the frozen River Stour from Richborough to the toll bridge at Sandwich.

A couple in Margate looked out of their flat at daybreak on 26th January and saw loose pack ice heading towards the shore. Mr Harry Heywood said it reminded him of the excitement of living in Antarctica. The moving ice, which had originated in the Swale or Medway, was a spectacular sight in a winter of rare beauty.

Just how unusual the winter had become could be measured by the number of days that snow lay on the ground. At Goudhurst there was snow cover on 65 days beating previous notable incidents such as in 1947, when the days of snow cover were 55. The normal pattern of wind over Britain was entirely reversed by persistent high pressure to the north and north-east bringing air off an icy Continent instead of from the warmer Atlantic Ocean.

By the third week of February the question people were asking was: "When will it end!" Another concern was for the danger of flooding; heavy rain following a thaw would bring conditions similar to those experienced in 1947. Several more inches of snow fell in West Kent during the evening of 22nd February but mercifully it was to be the last. The elements relented by providing a gentle day-time thaw at the month's end with dazzling sunshine and deep blue skies, though it remained frosty at night. By early March the snow was thinning, gently releasing several months of stored water.

Slowly the mercury rose and, by the end of the first week of March, Kent was verdant again.

The winter of 1963 was memorable, not only for persistent cold weather, but also for the beauty. Here is a typical January morning in a Kentish lane.

The winter of 1963 was one of the rare occasions when the River Stour at Sandwich froze over completely. The rise and fall of the tide is so great that the ice on the river is normally broken up as it begins to form. One of the most complete mediaeval towns in England, Sandwich lost its importance as a port with the siltation of the Wantsum Channel.

The Swinging, Shivering, Sixties

1960: Severe January snow-storms isolated the villages of Hastingleigh, Pluckley, Smarden and Postling. Two people were trapped for five hours in a snow-bound car on the outskirts of Dover. There were floods at Tonbridge due to the thawing snow and the Tudeley Road was impassable.

On Sunday 7th August customers in the Three Daws Inn, Gravesend's 500-year-old pub, were listening to the landlord call last orders when flood waters came swirling into the saloon bar. They jumped on to the counter to finish their drinks and then made their way home through the murky water.

1961: St Valentine's Day warmed the ardour of true love with 65F (18C) at Bromley.

1962: A night time air frost at Dartford on 3rd June. On the same day Margate could only muster 53F (12C).

1965: Summer and winter in one month. March started with a snow-storm and ended in a heat-wave with 72F (22C) at Chislehurst on 28th-29th.

1966: Severe January cold with -2F (-19C) at Elmstone was followed by a glaze caused by heavy rain falling with the temperature below freezing.

On 14th April a dry, powdery snow-fall caused a harrowing time for drivers on Polhill, south of Badger's Mount. Snow was six inches deep and the temperature was below freezing at Cudham around noon.

1967: Snow showers interrupted cricket matches in Avery Hill Park in early May. Ramsgate had a 27-day absolute drought in July.

1969: Local weathermen reported that the month of October was the warmest and driest ever recorded in Folkestone. The sun shone for a total of 148.7 hours and only half an inch (11.2 mm) of rain was recorded. This was followed by several inches of snow falling early in the season on 29th November causing lorries to become stuck at Bickley on the Southborough Road.

January 1963. Coal barges are frozen in the sea at Rochester.

Sad Story of the Kent Piers

WITH the exception of July 1967 when Thanet experienced a 27-day drought, the weather in the mid-60's was not notable for baking hot summer months. However, this did not stop hordes of people heading for the Kentish coastal resorts.

Many visited the famous old pier at Herne Bay which was the first to be built in Kent, in 1831, and the fifth in England.

The original pier was replaced in 1873 and a grand pavilion incorporated in 1910. One of the longest and most popular in the country, it was destined to meet its demise during the severe gales of 1978.

Many of Kent's old piers succumbed to the waves and the wind and after the second world war Deal alone rebuilt its pier, a typical mid-20th century structure of durability rather than grace. The original Deal pier, opened in 1866, was badly damaged by a storm-driven wreck in 1940 and demolished in 1954.

Folkestone Pier, built in 1867, was also breached in 1940 and then charred by fire in 1945. This once illustrious pier was left for many years as a blackened eyesore until it was demolished in 1952.

Margate Pier, built in 1853, was badly damaged in 1877 and 1897. Many happy years were to follow but the sea had the final word. In 1976 the authorities declared the pier unsafe and it was closed. Two years later it was washed away by the tidal surge of 1978.

Ramsgate Pier was opened in 1881. In 1917 it was damaged by fire and ship collision. In 1918 a mine was washed up beneath the pier and exploded. The result was a decaying, almost quaint skeleton, which disfigured the bustling Ramsgate sea front for many years. In 1929 possession passed to the Ministry of Transport and the eyesore was demolished.

Dover Pier, opened in 1893, was 900 feet long. In that same year a ship collided with it and further damage occurred a year later in a violent storm. It was re-opened in 1895 and a pavilion added just before the turn of the century. Like other piers it sustained a terrible battering by the elements and, in 1927, had to be demolished.

More than 20 vehicles blocked the road at Crockham Hill, near Westerham after a heavy fall of snow on 9th January, 1968. Some managed to slither up sideways. Others were stranded and it was some hours before the road was clear.

A Technicolour Surprise
1st July, 1968

IN what was a disappointing summer, a brief hot spell at the end of June and beginning of July brought a technicolour surprise to parts of Kent. A southerly air-flow, straight out of Africa, whipped up desert dust of fine sand and clay particles which travelled all the way to Britain at a height of around 14,000 feet and then fell, mixed with rain drops.

When drivers in Chislehurst and Bromley and other West Kent towns and villages went out to their newly cleaned cars, they were aghast. Red, orange and yellow spots covered the vehicles. It was estimated that several thousand tons of the Sahara fell on England that day.

108

The Wild, Wild Waters

15th September, 1968

IN the early hours of Sunday morning, 15th September, 1968, a few spots of rain pattered gently across the river valleys of Kent. A flash of lightning crackled through the sky and animals in fields, recognising the warning, instinctively sought shelter. A thunderous clap disturbed light sleepers but the majority of people merely turned over, oblivious to the fact that Kent was about to experience one of the most serious natural disasters of the century.

Some hours later those lush valleys, towns, villages, hamlets, farms and hundreds of acres of countryside were under many feet of water. Some 2,400 square miles had received as much as 400 tons of water per acre; fast-flowing flood-water that embraced everything within its reach. Vehicles floated away, so did furniture, television sets, clothing and debris - all mingled grotesquely with the carcasses of dead livestock.

The culprit was a depression which deepened rapidly to the south-west of Britain producing a pronounced trough of low pressure across Kent and Surrey along which there were large scale vertical motions of the atmosphere. Worse still, it remained stationary all day on 15th September. And that meant prolonged, heavy rain.

The approach of the trough was heralded by a violent storm around lunch-time on Saturday 14th. At Biggin Hill, during the annual "At Home" Day to commemorate the anniversary of the Battle of Britain, a Vulcan bomber was struck by lightning. Thunder cracks boomed across the much-bombed former fighter station, adding an eerie reality to the day's proceedings. The sun crept out in the afternoon and the show went on.

Later that evening and into the early hours of Sunday, the eastern horizon was lit up by more flashes of lightning. Rain began to fall. It quickly became a deluge and continued throughout the night and all the next day. The rivers of Kent could not cope with the sheer weight and speed of the water. Along the courses of the Medway, the Stour, the Ravensbourne, the Eden, the Darent, the Swale and all the tributaries, flood defences capitulated and vast lakes were created. Cars were swept away and people were trapped in upstairs rooms as the swirling brown floods hurtled on. Sewage spewed from blocked drains to form a sea of mud. Trees and shrubs were torn from the ground. Never for a moment did the rain cease. It poured down relentlessly from a leaden sky, hissing and bubbling as it landed, flooding areas which had never been flooded before. No town fared worse than Tonbridge where the River Medway overtopped the town bridge and surging flood-waters swept into the High Street. It slopped against doors and windows, burst them open and tugged goods from shelves and cupboards of practically every shop in the road. The damage ran into hundreds of thousands of pounds. By midnight on Sunday, a river of water five feet deep was gushing down the High Street and still the level of the Medway was rising. The town was cut in half. The police, the Fire Brigade, the Army, ambulance services, the WRVS and a host of volunteers co-operated in a massive rescue operation.

Amphibious vehicles took scores of families to places of safety. The elderly were rescued from bedrooms and hundreds of people stranded in cars, buses and coaches were given makeshift accommodation in local hotels. Communication was difficult. All telephone lines were out of operation; gas and electricity supplies were either cut or severely restricted. During the deluge the Cannon Lane bridge over the Medway collapsed and the main water supply pipes were washed away. A fleet of tankers carried water to hundreds of homes.

In the bright sunshine of Tuesday morning, 16th September hundreds of people gathered to look at the High Street. There were two groups at either end of the town. Between them was the river, still swirling into shops and washing away valuable stock. In the middle was a Kent and Sussex Courier van which floated out of a car park and was corralled by a policeman who lashed it to a signpost.

It was almost the same story in Maidstone. The rise of the River Medway was rapid and by mid-day on Sunday morning all low-lying areas of the town were flooded. But it was The Len which burst out of its culvert and made a clean east-west break in communications.

The dual carriageway at Detling, the A20 at Charing and the A228 at Leybourne were impassable. Broiler chickens were drowned at Birling, the railway embankment between Borough Green and Kemsing was washed away, 800 telephones were out of order, elderly people were rescued and the county town itself was just inches away from the greatest disaster of all. The Medway, now an enormous, powerful expanse, was lapping the arches of the Maidstone bridge. Water was filling the pedestrian subway and swirling up the High Street. As the floods grew, the boardwalks built by the Royal Engineers had to be extended. The town was closed and an emergency declared. With bated breath people waited for high tide at 9pm and the real crisis. It passed without further incident.

At Whitstable a large force of East Kent firemen saved the town from disaster when a reservoir near the harbour, known as The Backwater threatened to

The water was deep and still moving fast. It didn't stop two conscientious housewives splashing home through Edenbridge High Street with the barest of supplies.

flood 1,200 houses. Millions of gallons of storm water filled the reservoir and a county-wide alert went out for reinforcements as the firemen began pumping the water into the sea. Many streets were several feet deep and the Whitstable rescue boat, normally in service at sea, toured the flooded streets taking people to reception centres.

Whitstable was a town under siege. Police stopped all cars and advised motorists not to enter. Streets around the harbour were blocked with fire engines and the urban council mobilised all resources from its headquarters in Tankerton Castle.

People in Sevenoaks, 650 feet above sea level, had the un-nerving and almost unbelievable experience of seeing a river not far from the town centre. Rain, gathering in the valleys of Knole Park, suddenly burst through and, emulating a wild torrent surged down Seal Hollow Road. In the lower-lying areas, families waded chest deep to rescue belongings while others rowed in with hot food for those trapped in bedrooms.

One of the worst hit villages was Chipstead where 100 families were evacuated as the nearby lake burst its banks and swept through houses from back to front. A picturesque garden disappeared and a garage and car slid into the lake.

At Brasted, the whole of the village was under water. Torrents came rushing down from the hillsides.

It was the same story in Sundridge where the River Darent is usually little more than a tiny trickle. On Sunday 15th September the "trickle" became a full-scale river. It overtopped the sandbags and surged on towards Shoreham, completely covering the old stone bridge and isolating the village.

In Otford High Street, the bridge over the Darent was swept away in the early hours of Monday 16th. People brought out rubber dinghies and small boats but soon abandoned them in the unmanageable torrent. In Westerham the flood waters rushed down from the surrounding hillsides. From Toys Hill, from Hosey and Biggin Hill, the meeting point was Quebec Square where General Wolfe, his sword aloft, looked like an abandoned soldier with the enemy closing in.

Dartford was flooded, of course. Needing only a "minor incident" to go under, the North Kent town stood no chance as the Darent burst its banks and torrential water fed the streams under the High Street. Sittingbourne and Faversham had the worst floods for 15 years but, compared to other parts of Kent, escaped fairly lightly. Herne Bay Pier, the second longest in England, was closed, believed to be unsafe.

A lorry with "passengers" perched high above the floods; a tractor and soldiers of the Royal Engineers in a dinghy negotiated the inundations in Edenbridge as the mopping up continued.

It was to survive just another ten years.

The only fatality was in Ashford where Mr Robert Bennett, aged 66, died from a heart attack when flood water knocked him off his feet as it shot across Ashford Road and poured into a lane where he was walking. The miracle of this disaster was that no-one else died.

From the air, the Medway Valley looked like a massive lake with factories, churches, oasts, farmhouses and the tops of apple trees floating in the middle. Yalding was under water. So were Laddingford, East Peckham, Paddock Wood, Wateringbury, Teston and Tudeley. Older people in the Medway valley were used to such conditions - but this time they demanded immediate action. No-one should be expected to suffer like this again.

Perhaps the greatest drama of the day belonged to the town of Edenbridge where the bridge over the River Eden was submerged and the town centre inundated with swirling, murky water which rose, in places, to roof-top height. During Sunday afternoon three people, Mr and Mrs Albert Young and their 20-year-old daughter Sue, were marooned next door to their shop, Bridge Stores, which was being torn to pieces by the current.

A lifeline was taken out by Mr Ken Humphries who secured it near the shop and sat on a totally submerged tractor keeping control of the line. Two men took a boat to the shop and rescued Sue. They went back for her mother and urged her to jump. She did, the boat overturned and all three were thrown into the current. Mrs Young managed to cling onto the pillar in the shop and somehow clambered back upstairs. One of the men followed her. The other man, Mr Kimber, a retired fireman, disappeared and was feared drowned. He re-appeared and spent the next 30 minutes clinging onto posts and being washed from one roof to another. He eventually made it to the shop. A second boat was sent for and, after some hours, all three were rescued.

Meanwhile, Mr Ken Humphries was sitting on the tractor in his skinsuit holding the lifeline to the boats

No deliveries today. This was Fairdale Stores at Borough Green.

which went in relays to rescue people trapped on the east side of the High Street. He remained there for six and a half hours.

More drama was to follow. A train from Charing Cross to Hastings was diverted to Edenbridge because British Rail officials thought it was clear of floods. How wrong they were. The line was blocked with five feet of flood water and 80 passengers sat on the train watching the water still rising.

As darkness fell, a Whirlwind helicopter from air-sea rescue at Manston took the passengers supplies of food and drinks. The army then ordered 10 assault craft to move to Edenbridge to rescue the stranded travellers.

In every Kentish town cut off by floods, rescue and reception centres were quickly set up by the police, the WRVS, women's institutes, Red Cross, Salvation Army and other voluntary organisations. Fire and Ambulance Services were overstretched and undermanned but received invaluable assistance from reservists. The Great Flood of 1968 was over, but for many weeks there was the heart-breaking work of mopping up, drying out and repairing and rebuilding damage caused by the most torrential rain Kent has ever known. There was Government aid for many of those in distress.

The most urgent task concerned the repair and the strengthening of the river defences. As usual with such a massive disaster the cry went out from all corners of Kent: "It must never happen again".

Tonbridge High Street where flood waters from the River Medway slopped into every shop in the town centre between the town bridge and the Angel Hotel. Many of the shop windows were initially broken by the wave created by an army dukw.

*Water covered the little stone bridge over the Medway at Teston between Maidstone and Wateringbury.
Normally the bridge is at least 10 feet above water level.*

The village of Chipstead, near Sevenoaks, where the nearby lake burst it banks and 100 residents were evacuated.

Chaos came to Bromley in the wake of the floods. Telephone lines were out of action, electricity supplies cut and rail services cancelled. An elderly lady was taken ill with fright when she saw three feet of water in her hall. Many were rescued from upstairs rooms as the Ravensbourne transformed nearby roads into a lake. The photograph was taken in Widmore Road, Bromley.

These two cars were swept by flood water for 75 yards from aptly named Watery Lane, Kemsing, into a nearby field. The drivers, from West Kingsdown and Ightham, managed to scramble out and splash their way to safety.

Hever Castle, the home of Lord and Lady Astor, and the Tudor village were invaded by the waters of the River Eden.

19th February, 1969. A severe easterly gale accompanied by snow produced 12 inches in Deal and isolated many villages. This photograph taken between Deal and Dover, shows an abandoned traffic jam.

Just Two Candles Each

4th March, 1970

A deepening depression embedded in a cold polar airstream moved south-east across England on the night of 4th March, 1970, enveloping Kent in a thick snowstorm. Power lines were brought down blacking out homes and trapping hundreds of miners below ground in the East Kent coalfield.

Among the worst affected districts were Romney Marsh, the Elham Valley and Folkestone. The transmission lines at Dungeness "A" nuclear power station were severed and the plant had to be shut down. Six inches of ice had built up around some of the cables. Others clashed together in the high winds giving rise to a blinding flash and a complete break of the wire. In all, some 100 miles of overhead cable were brought to earth.

By evening, after a day of relentless snow, all efforts were concentrated on restoring power to the three coal mines. Hundreds of miners had found themselves trapped underground when the electrically-driven lifts became inoperative.

Folkestone Water Company's main pumping stations were also put out of action and employees worked all night manning the back-up diesel engines.

The snow fell so thickly that, in spite of the efforts of five snow-ploughs and six lorries, hundreds of cars were abandoned and troops from Shorncliffe Garrison were called in to move stranded vehicles. Drifts more than eight feet deep were reported in some places.

For more than four days some parts of the hardest hit area south of Ashford had no power or telephone lines and here candles were rationed two to a house.

The Welling Whirlwind

25th January, 1971

A typical winter mix of fresh south-westerly winds and showers characterised Monday 25th January, 1971. There was nothing unusual in this, yet during the late afternoon there was a spate of calls to the emergency services. Windows had been sucked out, roofs had gaping holes and walls had come tumbling down.

Two mechanics working on a car at the rear of Douglas Barnes Autos in Church Road, Welling, dived for cover when they saw large chunks of guttering and tiles hurtling through the air. A dustbin was thrown through the back window of one of the vehicles.

Mr Alec Bird, manager of the Clive Stuart Cycle Shop in Bellgrove Road, was serving a customer when he heard a mighty roar. Suddenly his shop window was drawn out along with four or five bicycles. Dustbins were whirling through the air along with shirts from a nearby clothing shop.

The culprit was a tornado, a violent vortex of air around which winds can exceed hurricane force with much reduced air pressure at its centre, which can cause windows to bulge outwards and roofs to be lifted off. It was first identified off the Isle of Wight where a waterspout was seen approaching the coast. Making landfall, it removed an arm of a signpost but no further damage was reported until it reached Avery Hill, Eltham.

More than 100 shops, homes and offices suffered varying amounts of damage in a swathe often no more than 150 yards wide. Mr Edward Heath, who was Prime Minister and MP for Bexley, wrote to the Mayor expressing his sympathy.

Helicopter Rescue

September 27, 1973

AMONG the many stories of the sea, none is more unusual than that told by Margate photographer Chris Fright who has supplied many of the pictures for this book.

On 27th September, 1973 Chris was filming routine coast-guard activities for the children's TV programme, Newsround, when vicious autumn gales swept in, reaching Force 10. The helicopter, piloted by Flight Lieutenant Clive Chandler with an RAF Crew, put Chris down on top of 500 foot cliffs but conditions were too severe so they picked him up and the men took off again - this time for the Goodwin Sands.

By now Chris was hoping to get good photographs of the storm but what he saw below was even more dramatic. Four people were clinging on to a Catamaran which was being smashed to pieces by giant waves.

The RAF immediately took up rescue positions and a winch was lowered into the current. The first to come up was a boy of seven in bad shape, followed by his brother aged nine. Two men, almost unconscious, were saved, one holding a dog. Chris Fright filmed the entire drama which was shown that night on the BBC Nine o'clock News.

This dramatic photograph taken by Margate photographer Chris Fright shows two boys and one of the men clinging desperately to what was left of their Catamaran which was being smashed to pieces by giant waves.

Vintage Year for Kent Cricket

IN 1970, its centenary year, Kent Cricket Club won the County Championship for the first time since 1913. This was followed by eight glorious years in which the club won the championship on two more occasions, the Sunday League three times and knock-out cup contests four times.

These were vintage years for cricket enthusiasts and the long hot summers, particularly in 1975 and 1976, played a memorable part in the renaissance of Kent cricket.

In 1977 Kent was well on the way towards winning the championship outright when the weather suddenly turned and played a cruel hand. Two days were washed out at Canterbury and the game at Colchester was abandoned without a ball being bowled. On this occasion the weather won and Kent had to be content to share the honours with Middlesex.

February 1974 and the Medway Valley at Yalding is under water again. Cars and caravans were afloat as well as boats. John Mellor, the Kent Messenger photographer, climbed a sixty foot tower to take this picture.

31st January, 1976. Famous for its blazing heat, 1976 also saw "pancake" ice floes on the River Stour, at Sandwich, during a short, sharp and very cold spell at the end of January.

The Blazing Summer of 1976

FEW weather events have captured the attention of the media, public and politicans so much as the drought of 1976. We were told by at least one national paper to put a brick into our toilet cisterns or even share a bath with a friend. For 16 consecutive days the temperature somewhere in England reached or exceeded 90F (32C) - an unprecedented event. With much of Kent receiving less than 60 per cent of its average rainfall between May 1975 and August 1976 this represented the worst drought since 1727 when rainfall records of any accuracy were first kept.

At Tunbridge Wells the temperature reached 82F (28C) as early as 7th May, a taste of things to come. By 26th June 93F (34C) was recorded and similar readings occurred on 3rd July but it was the continuing lack of rain throughout the summer which made weather history. Biddenden had no rain at all in June.

Kent became tinder dry. Fires broke out right across the county with 161 calls for assistance on 7th July alone. It meant hard-pressed fire crews were often in action a long way from base. For instance, crews from Herne Bay and Whitstable fought grass fires in and around the Medway Towns.

In early July 13,000 tons of baled paper and pulp caught fire at the Reed International Paper Mills at Aylesford. Over 100 firemen fought bravely amid thick smoke and searing heat to control the blaze.

At Chatham, an old Napoleonic Fort containing thousands of rubber tyres was in the path of a grass fire. This resulted in the near destruction of the building and a huge pall of thick, black smoke which could be seen as far away as Maidstone.

Potentially the most dangerous episode was at Lydd Army Range. As in other areas, shrub and woodland caught fire but on this occasion a hail of exploding ammunition made it a harrowing ordeal for the fire brigade and soldiers. Firemen had to avoid spraying water close to high tension electricity lines as this could have conducted fatal shocks to the men on the ground. The danger was exacerbated by the proximity of the Dungeness Nuclear Power Station. The reactors were switched off and the whole area was enveloped in clouds of smoke. It was six hours before the flames were finally brought under control.

During the summer the damage to the Kent countryside was immense. At West Blean Woods, Herne, thousands of young fir trees were destroyed in a blaze that raged for four days,involving most of the crews in East Kent. Directly in the path of the conflagration lay Westlands Holiday Camp. It was only a change of wind that saved the already evacuated centre.

As the drought continued there were 36 consecutive rainless days at Sidcup. The crisis deepened. A satellite picture taken on 21st August showed Britain devoid of cloud and the mercury rose yet again to the high eighties Fahrenheit (30C).

Emergency measures of all kinds were put into practice. Bars of sea-water soap were on sale in some resorts. It lathered in salt water so one could take a bath in the sea and avoid the water restrictions. Kent, however, fared better in this respect than counties further west such as Devon. Even so, hosepipes, sprinklers and any large-scale use of water was banned. This really seemed to have put the damper on the annual "It's a Knockout" carnival at Sittingbourne. A "Greasy Pole" contest, moistened by a thousand gallons of water, was normally one of the star attractions, but not this year, until somebody realised that an unlimited supply lay just two miles away. A local firm volunteered to bring in sea water by tanker when it was assured that it would do no harm to either the contestants or the town's recreation ground. The show was able to go on.

Ironically, as parts of Britain were suffering a Mediterranean-like summer, reports came in from Hong Kong that it had been ravaged by Typhoon Ellen. A colossal 16inches (420mm) of rain fell in 24 hours - almost two-thirds of Kent's yearly quota in one day!

In a state of desperation, one water authority wrote to the Department of Cloud Physics in New South Wales asking for information on rainmaking. In London, a guru prayed for rain while the government finally sensing the urgency of the situation played its trump card and appointed a Minister for Drought, Mr Dennis Howell. Almost as though it had a sense of humour, the weather gave way. The persistent block of high pressure broke down. The development of an upper trough to the south-west of Britain combined with unusually high sea-surface temperatures led to September being the second wettest over England since the early eighteenth century. At Dover more than 8 inches (200 mm) fell and the rains continued. The transformation was reflected in figures from Sevenoaks. January to August brought only 6 inches (160mm(, while the three following months yielded 12 inches (313 mm). The crisis was simply washed away.

Hythe under threat

During a weekend of tempestuous storms on 9th and 10th February, 1974, the Dungeness lifeboat was launched in 80mph winds, hundreds of acres of farmland were flooded in the Biddenden and Rolvenden areas, trees were uprooted near Ashford and inundated coast roads closed. Hythe was particularly under threat. When roads were re-opened on Monday, this Hythe motorist (see left) was still in danger of being engulfed.

8th July, 1976. The front page of the Chatham News which reported the dramatic blaze at the Old Napoleonic Fort.

July 1976. As the sun continued to shine without any sign of a break, outdoor lessons became a way of life for pupils all over the county. These children are from St John's School, Sevenoaks.

Reservoirs throughout the county dried up. Bough Beech, near Four Elms, is well known to ornithologists for its wide variety of resident and visiting birds, including the osprey. By August 1976 the situation had become grave with very little water for either the birds or the consumers of East Surrey Water Company.

Storm Force at Deal

11th-12th January 1978

THE first week of 1978 saw some rain, a little sunshine and occasional night frost. Nothing out of the ordinary - but things were to change rapidly. What the meteorologists call a "wave" on the weather front deepened into an intense depression, which on the 11th January crossed the Midlands and East Anglia. In its wake a severe northerly gale whipped up a tidal surge that was almost as bad as that of 1953. East Kent took the brunt of the storm as winds gusted well in excess of 80 mph.

The awesome power of the wind and wave was felt at Margate where the old pier was finally reduced to piles of contorted girders, with the lifeboat station stranded at the seaward end. Fortunately the rescue vessel was retrieved. Herne Bay pier was also destroyed, reduced to matchwood and piled high on the beach.

All along the coast it was a night of high drama. At Deal the tumultuous sea crashed over the defences forcing the evacuation of 100 people. Huge masses of shingle were swept in by every wave. The terror of the night was experienced by Mr Len Hunt as giant waves crashed against his house at The Marina. First smashing the windows and then tearing down the front door, the water swept in battering the furniture and cutting the electricity supply. The mayhem was complete in seconds. In a nearby basement flat the ceiling collapsed onto 87-year-old Tom Stanley who was taken to hospital with lacerations. At another house, thousands of pounds worth of antique furniture was destroyed.

Daylight revealed the full scale of the night-time ferment. Boats, some damaged beyond repair, littered the foreshore and one was tossed and laid to rest outside the Regent Bingo House (see also page 102). Boat winches, weighing up to three tons, were torn from their moorings. Snow-ploughs were used to force a path through mountains of shingle in Sandown Road. At Athelston Place, which was five feet deep in water, boats were used to rescue elderly citizens.

At the Chequers Inn, Sandown, eight people were cut off by the rising tide. They lit a fire on the roof to attract attention and then retired to the top floor. Gusts of wind of hurricane force prevented an RAF rescue helicopter from taking off at Manston and a similar bid by the Royal Marines using a "Gemini" launch also ended in failure. On land, police and Army firefighters had to abandon their assault as they were beaten back by the icy flood-waters in Golf Road.

So it was that a frightening and uncomfortable night was spent in the isolated inn amid the swirling waters, the whine and screech of the raging storm and the all-pervading thunderous roar of the sea. Eventually, some time after dawn, a local farmer with a tractor-trailer laboriously made his way through the deep water and rescued the occupants, now suffering from shock and exposure.

When the winds finally abated the clear-up cost Kent some £5 million. The City of London narrowly escaped a major disaster as water came to within 19 inches of the top of the retaining walls. The lessons of this storm were to reinforce the need to complete the Thames Flood Barrier downstream at Greenwich.

A Window on the Seventies

1970: A classic white Christmas. Chislehurst and Bromley had eight inches of snow with a loud clap of thunder on Christmas night.

1971: Heavy rain and high tides caused havoc in many coastal towns on 28th July, 1971. Firemen from Dover, Deal, Folkestone, Hythe, Whitstable and Dymchurch worked non-stop for 16 hours, pumping out houses and rescuing trapped people.

1972: A brief but severe cold spell in late January sent the mercury down to 0F (-18C) at East Malling. The longest day of the year, 21st June, was also one of the coldest on record for East Kent. Temperatures struggled only to 58.6F (14C) by day and farmers reported that the cold spell would have a serious effect on hay-making. On 12th-13th November a Force 11 storm across south-east Kent injured two people, leaving a trail of broken windows and toppled trees in its wake.

1973: On 19th September an electric storm over Folkestone, Hythe and Romney Marsh damaged a transformer, brought down an overhead conductor line and caused thousands of homes to be blacked out, including all of Lydd, Elham and Stelling Minnis. Residents spoke of a vertical curtain of lightning accompanied by torrential rain. The following day, 20th September, a small but active low pressure area deepened as it crossed northern France and produced record rainfall in the extreme east of the county. At Manston, 6.67 inches (170mm) fell in just 24 hours.

The lifeboat station at the far end of Margate pier is marooned 500 yards out to sea. The pier itself, broken in three sections, is submerged beneath the waves.

1974: A whirlwind swept across part of Folkestone on 23rd September in a very unsettled month, but December was unusually mild and Sevenoaks recorded several days warmer than the previous July.

1975: On New Year's Day the Folkestone Herald reported that, in the Shepway district, spring flowers were in bloom after the mildest Christmas for 22 years. During the week ending Saturday, 28th December, maximum temperatures never dropped below 50F (10C). At the beginning of June a bitterly cold arctic airstream swept south over Kent. Snowflakes were seen at Orpington and the temperature fell below freezing at Paddock Wood. Just a week later the mercury soared to 80F (27C) over most of the county.

1977: In June, whilst the temperature on the French and Belgium coast reached 90F (32c) it struggled to reach 68F (20C) at Westerham. This large range of temperature triggered off spectacular storms on two successive nights 12th-13th June. Intense rainfall led to flooding from the River Cray at Sidcup. On 27th August an afternoon cloudburst caused severe flooding in Orpington, Lock's Bottom and St Paul's Cray. Mr Paul Gurley of St Mary's Cray recorded 3.56 inches (89 mm) on his rain gauge during the storm. For August that year he recorded 7.28 inches (182mm), roughly one quarter of the average year's rainfall for that area.

1978: Snow and icy roads were responsible for three fatal accidents involving cars in Maidstone, Margate and Hawkhurst on the same day, 19th January.

Heavy waves pound the sea front at the end of Central Parade, Herne Bay.

A far cry from the summer crowds that throng the sands at Herne Bay. The remains of the famous old pier litter the beach.

SPECIAL STORM EDITION

East Kent Mercury

DEAL AND SANDWICH NEWS

ON THE SPOT
PICTURES
AND
STORIES

No. 5848 | FRIDAY, JANUARY 13, 1978 | Price 5p

NIGHT OF TERROR AS FLOODS HIT DEAL

DISASTER struck Deal in the early hours of yesterday (Thursday). Damage estimated at over £1½m was caused in less than two hours when hundreds of homes were flooded as sea water crashed over the defences. Many people had to be rescued from their bedrooms.

Winds reached hurricane force in the early hours of the morning and at high tide, the sea swept tons of shingle over the seawall and seafront.

Dozens of boats were damaged beyond repair and the beach was torn to pieces. The storm uprooted street lights like matchsticks.

The worst hit areas were in North Deal, at College Road, The Marina and Athelstan Place, and at Kingsdown. During the day, more than 100 people were evacuated from their flooded homes, and 500 properties were without electricity.

Seafront homes suffered severe damage not only from flooding but from the sheer weight of shingle pushed into the houses by the heavy seas.

The flooding and damage was the worst for 25 years and emergency services were stretched to capacity.

Old people had to be evacuated from nursing homes and old folks' homes and many were accommodated at the Royal Marines Infirmary. The Royal Marines were also making plans to help other homeless families.

When the notices were first put up in Deal High Street, they referred to the traffic. But in the early hours of yesterday morning they took on a new meaning as the water flooded the street, "One Way Flow Reversed".

A Royal Marine fixes an outboard motor to the "Gemini" dinghy in which he tried to reach the stranded people at the Chequers Inn at Sholden.

'Trapped on roof' of a pub

BIG DRAMA of the night was at The Chequers Inn, which stands on the Sandhills at Deal.

Kent Police received a report in the early hours of yesterday (Thursday) morning that the building was on fire, and that people were trapped on the roof.

There was another report that the public house was flooded, and that the residents had taken to the roof for safety.

Dover Strait Coastguards were also alerted, and so were the crew of the R.A.F. rescue helicopter at Manston. But the weather was too rough for the helicopter to attempt a rescue.

Police and Army firefighters on the Green Goddess "Alpha Foxtrot 4" attempted to get to the Chequers, but found their way blocked by flood water in Golf Road.

At one stage the Army crew reported 10 feet of water.

SHOCK

The Royal Marines brought in a "Gemini" rubber dinghy in another attempt to gain access to the trapped people. But this also failed.

It was not until well after daybreak that Mr. Peter Hambrook, of Solley's Farm, got through to the Chequers with a tractor and trailer, and took a number of people to safety, all suffering from shock and exposure.

Among them was 21-year-old Sharon Humphreys, the daughter of the licensees of the Chequers, Mr. and Mrs. Bob Humphreys.

Another warning

A "D" flood warning — the next to highest warning issued—was broadcast just before the high water yesterday lunchtime. It was feared that this might be even higher than the early morning tide.

But the wind appeared to have decreased a little, and this helped to reduce the impact of the second tide.

Fire Brigade headquarters were taking no chances, however, and just after 2 p.m. yesterday, they despatched their "flight column"—five Green Goddesses from Maidstone and a mobile control unit—to stand by at Alfred Square.

Ambulancemen worked through the night and day, driving through flood water to evacuate people. These two ambulances are pictured in the northern end of College Road.

Quite a task for a welder! This car was left to the mercy of the waves that pounded the promenade at Herne Bay.

There was a mountain of shingle and debris on the foreshore at Deal. Snow-ploughs were used to force a path through.

There was no shortage of water to float these craft at Oare Creek, near Faversham.

The flat, windswept village on the extreme tip of the Hoo Peninsular is called Grain. In blizzard conditions it can be exceptionally bleak as shown by this photograph, taken in January 1979, during a hunt for buried cars. This was the "winter of discontent" when many factories were shut due to strikes. At Edenbridge, a shivering picket-line huddled around makeshift bonfires at a print-works — a sight repeated across the county. In mid-February, blizzards and sub-zero temperatures returned. Snow-ploughs helped clear the M25 motorway.

Mild and Bitter

1970-1983

AFTER the deep snows of Christmas 1970, winters in the following decade were relatively benign with a notable absence of snow. In fact the winter of 1974-5 was the mildest for more than 100 years.

However, the winter of 1978 was memorable. A severe gale during the night of 11th-12th January was accompanied by heavy snow in West Kent. There was a repeat performance in February and on the 9th, blizzard conditions created large corniced drifts on the roads to Ide Hill and Toys Hill. Late snow was experienced on 10th April with seven inches in Orpington.

The year ended with severe cold and a snowstorm on 30th December, 1978. New Year 1979 brought tragedy. An elderly couple abandoned their car near Stalisfield Green, Faversham and went their separate ways through deep powdery snow in search of help. The man was later found dead near a telephone box.

The arctic conditions of 1979 continued into February when a surge of bitter air spread south-west from Scandinavia. The Isle of Sheppey was cut off by deep snow-drifts. De-icing trains and snow-ploughs battled all night to clear the Maidstone to Ashford line but they were thwarted by constantly drifting snow. Even as late as May the winter was not over as several inches of snow settled on the downs above Westerham.

There were just a few flurries in 1980 but in December 1981 a full-scale blizzard swept across the country, forcing the Queen to seek shelter in a Cotswold Inn. Snow on the 22nd closed Bluebell Hill and many places in Kent experienced snow on the ground for Christmas Day. During this month Gillingham had snow cover for 22 days.

In January 1982 England had a new low temperature record of — 15F (-26C) in Shropshire. Pegwell Bay was frozen over and the M2 suffered a 10-mile tailback as snow swept across the motorway.

Jutting out as it does into the North Sea, East Kent is particularly susceptible to heavy snow in a cold northerly airstream with lighter falls further west. In what was a mild winter overall, the wind turned northerly on 7th February, 1983 bringing atrocious conditons to the Folkestone, Dover and Sandwich area. As the snow piled up, only 18 out of 960 pupils turned up for lessons at Archers Court School. Dover was cut off and bus services ground to a halt. Level snow in places was nearly 18 inches deep.

Does lightning strike twice__ The answer is yes, frequently. On 24th June, 1973 a house in Otford was struck by fork lightning. On exactly the same day seven years later the same house was struck again during a week of localised thunderstorms in the Sevenoaks area.

Torrential rain did not stop these people from greeting the Queen Mother when she visited Knole, Sevenoaks on 23rd June, 1980 for an early 80th birthday celebration.

Intense Storm Surprises Sevenoaks

25th June, 1980

ONE of the Queen Mother's 80th birthday parties was at Knole House, Sevenoaks on Monday 23rd June, 1980. It was notable on two counts - the radiance and charm of the principal guest and the heavy downpour of rain which greeted the royal party. It was, in fact, the start of an unsettled week with frequent thundery showers, but the storm that was to hit Sevenoaks at 4.15 on Wednesday 25th June took everyone by surprise.

In less than two hours 4.15 inches (116.1mm) of rain and hail fell on the town centre, making it one of the most intense local storms on record. Meteorologist Peter Rogers, whose station was on the outskirts of both town and storm, recorded 2.1 inches (52.8 mm). A mile further north at the Crampton's Road pumping station, the headquarters of West Kent Water Company, the total was a mere 0.8 of an inch (20 mm). In Shoreham village five miles away, there was no rain at all.

During that last week of June 1980, complex deep low pressure systems were centred near the north of

Scotland and thunderstorms were widespread. It was the town of Sevenoaks, however, which was to earn its place in the history books with rain and hail that left motorists stranded, shops and houses under water and homes in darkness as power supplies failed.

The sky, on this mid-summer afternoon, turned grey and then black as the temperature plunged from 63F (17C) to 43F (6C) in just half an hour. There was very little wind and the hailstorm moved slowly. This was the nineteenth consecutive day on which it had rained — and that was another record.

In the town centre the two inches of hailstones which fell had to be removed the next day by council workmen. At Sevenoaks railway station the line and platforms were covered with water and station staff were treated to the unusual sight of bowler-hatted commuters rolling up the legs of their pin-stripes and removing their shoes to wade through the floods.

Investigations suggested that this storm, although not as intense as the great storm of Hampstead, London, in August 1975, may rank among the three or four most intense local storms on record.

The junction of London Road and High Street, Sevenoaks during the height of the extraordinary mid-summer storm on 25th June, 1980. Within minutes the road was inches deep in ice. The storm ranks among the three or four most intense local storms on record.

Water Spout off The Leas

19th September 1981

A vortex of water, which was sucked from the sea into heavy clouds, moved along the coast off Folkestone and swept past the harbour before disappearing off Capel. This was a water spout, like a mini tornado at sea, and it lasted for 30 minutes at the most. People walking on the Leas witnessed this dramatic sight. A water spout in the Channel during the summer months was not uncommon but it was unusual for one to form only a few hundreds yards out to sea.

135

Sandgate Esplanade has seen many great storms but the one that breached defences and demolished the sea wall in 1981 was described by the Folkestone Herald as Sandgate's "worst storm in living memory". This photograph was taken on Sunday 13th December as the gale reached its zenith.

A Nightmare for Shepway

13th December, 1981

LESS than four years after the tidal surge of 1978 which mutilated defences in neighbouring coastal towns, it was Shepway's turn to experience the power of the waves. Throughout the heavy gale of Sunday 13th December, frothy seas became more and more agitated, leaping up and crashing down from ever-increasing heights. At midnight the waves broke through, tore sea defences to shreds and, in Sandgate, cascaded through the roofs of homes on the Esplanade.

One wave sent furniture rushing around on a flood of water, another swept away wooden shutters protecting windows and a third set alight electric cables. All along the coast residents were evacuated as firemen and workmen from Shepway District Council struggled to cope. One fireman was lifted off his feet by a wave which then dumped him on the Esplanade. He got up and walked away.

An elderly Sandgate flood victim knocked on the window of a house in the High Street on that bitterly cold night and asked for help. She was invited inside and for the next few hours a steady stream of tired, wet and bedraggled residents were given hot coffee and food.

Described by the Folkestone Herald as "Shepway's worst storm in living memory", the damage amounted to more than £1,100,000. Thirty houses were virtually destroyed and another 100 flooded. The Sandgate sea wall was torn apart.

February, 1985 and Pegwell Bay is frozen again with sightseers walking across the ice.

Fog Disaster

A capricious patch of fog on the M25 was blamed for an horrific crash between Westerham and Oxted in the early hours of 11th December, 1984. In what was then Britain's worst motorway disaster, nine people were killed.

The accident, which took place over a six minute period, involved 22 vehicles. It happened at 6.05 am in dark and patchy fog when lorries and cars piled into each other, some compressed into a fraction of their normal size.

It was the seventh time fog had caused an accident on this notorious stretch of the M25, which runs through the Holmesdale Valley south of the North Downs, and it prompted this warning from the AA: "Fog disorientates you. It's like driving along in a box. The heater and the radio are on and you can't see trees, hedges or any landmarks".

Walking on the Ice

JANUARY 1985 was the coldest, over most of Kent, since the infamous 1963 winter. At Jubilee Corner near Ashford the cold registered just 3F (-16C). Deep snow lay in the Lyminge Forest and around Doddington on the North Downs. A police car was abandoned near Hythe and a helicopter flying from Sevenoaks to Deal became caught up in a "white out" and was forced to land at The Strand, Gillingham. Pegwell Bay froze again and sightseers walked out across the ice in another cold spell in February.

The following year, 1986, produced one of those rare events which is deemed a "freezing month" to rival any this century; average temperatures failed to exceed 32F (0C). Although snowfall was mainly light it remained on the ground for more than three weeks.

So severe was the cold that a consultant geriatrician at Orpington Hospital reported 12 cases of hypothermia. February 1986 produced nothing warmer than 37F (3C) at Wigmore, Gillingham. Age Concern sent out 1,000 Cold Crisis Kits, which included a body warmer and a fuel voucher. Not surprisingly it proved to be the second coldest February so far this century.

Probably the most bizarre episode took place near Sittingbourne on the M2 motorway. Soon after a 50 car pile-up was cleared, cars were hurtling along in snowy conditions close on 100mph, according to Kent Police. Even these foolhardy road users were to find conditions virtually impossible the following year when Kent drew national and even world attention when, first snow and then storm brought the working day to a halt.

Walking on the Top of Hedges

January 1987

JANUARY 1987 will long be remembered for the blizzards and exceptional cold which paralysed the county. Snow, whipped up into drifts more than 15 feet deep, isolated many rural villages and even the M2 was blocked for nearly a week.

The bitter weather arrived from Russia and Scandinavia on Saturday 10th January. Icy winds brought snow showers throughout the day and penetrating frost that night. By the next day heavy snow lay several inches thick, blanketing the county with a deep white mantle and heralding the arrival of even bleaker weather. By Monday morning the temperature had dropped to a bone-chilling 9F (-13C) at breakfast time. Motorists found they could only see out of their windows by scraping frost off the inside of the glass. In the early afternoon temperatures rose only to 18F (-8C), making it the coldest day since 1867.

Further snow fell that evening and by the morning of Tuesday 13th, many roads were impassable. It was the Medway towns and villages in the north of Kent which bore the brunt of the frequent snow-showers coming in off the sea and Thames estuary. Ferocious easterly winds blew the snow into huge drifts on Wednesday 14th, blocking many roads, railways and town centres. Visibility was reduced to just a few feet as the clouds of icy crystals were blasted off fields by the vicious gusts.

The RAF and the Army were involved in operations to help villagers cut off by mountainous snow-drifts. At the Kent police headquarters in Maidstone an RAF Chinook helicopter air-lifted an Army Land Rover to a stricken village near Rochester. Seven Green Goddess fire tenders were brought out of mothballs to help the county's brigade reach isolated villages. At one stage, 160 calls a day were being answered.

By 14th January parts of Kent had a level snow depth of 29 inches, but reports of 18 inches were more widespread. The heaviest snow accumulations were in the west and north of Kent, with Dartford, Gravesend, Sevenoaks and Westerham particularly badly hit. The level depth at Orpington was 18 inches, at Gillingham 19 inches and across the Thames at Southend, 21 inches.

The Kentish Express reported that villagers in Hastingleigh, Elmstead and Bodsham, near Ashford, experienced the worst weather for over 20 years. By Thursday night on 15th January, snow had blocked all exits and a bitter wind had built up drifts making most roads impassable. One resident told the newspaper, "It is just like Siberia — if we do go out, we find ourselves walking on the tops of hedges".

Three Newchurch men made a 10-hour trek across snow-covered fields in a bid to bring provisions from New Romney — an eight-mile round trip. Worried neighbours alerted emergency services when Frank Knight, David Bailey and Mr Bailey's son Carl, were feared missing. A search party set out, led by Mr Knight's son, Graham. They found only deep snowdrifts. A helicopter called in to assist also failed to locate them. Fortunately, as darkness fell, the "missing" men returned home safe but cold and exhausted and with little to show for their efforts.

Local hospitals ran short of blood and emergency donor sessions were arranged to supply the William Harvey Hospital. The response to the SOS was good. Three hundred students from the police training college at Kennington were among the donors.

One of the first snow-bound patients to arrive at the William Harvey by helicopter was a mother and newly born baby. The baby, Marc, had been born to Karen Askey of Smarden in the presence of a mid-wife who managed to get through by tractor. A second helicopter brought Nellie Batchelor, aged 87, into hospital from Smarden.

Singer and DJ Judge Dread was motoring home to Snodland along the M20 when he was flagged down by the police and reprimanded. He was told if he drove another yard he would be booked for dangerous driving because of the appalling conditions.

About 60 people had to be rescued from their cars and lorries stranded on the A20 at Lenham when drifting snow blocked the road and buried their vehicles to such a depth it was impossible to open the doors. Police called in the Army to help liberate the trapped drivers. Some were entombed in six feet of snow but managed to be dragged out. Many spent the night at the Three Musketeers motel on the A20. The guests who were already booked in joined forces with the owner, Mr Tom Riley, in forming a rescue party to free other drivers, who risked spending the ferocious night of 14th January in their vehicles.

Several people lost their lives as a result of the bitter weather. At Hawkhurst, elderly Mr Charles Hall of Woodbine Villas collapsed and died after going outside to sweep his path of snow in the exceptional cold of 12th January.

A slight thaw was on the way, however, and the giant icicles which had formed on houses and shop fronts began to melt on the foggy morning of Monday 19th. As Kent unfroze life gradually returned to normal on the roads. For householders, though, there was worse to come. As frozen pipes thawed out bursts became evident and there was much flooding to follow. The Green Goddess fire tenders once again came to the rescue.

Few trains were running owing to snow and ice on the lines. Here commuters arrive at Gillingham after an eventful journey from the capital.

Many Kentish communities were isolated during the blizzard of January, 1987 and queues began to form outside village shops. Here, at Burham, people wait patiently for the Vale Bakery to open.

The weary trudge home with essential supplies. This is Dargetts Hill, Chatham.

The M20, closed by the police during the blizzard of January, 1987.

British Rail sent its famous Scottish snow-blower down from the Highlands to clear the line near Hoo so that oil supplies could get through from the refineries at Grain.

The Medway valley between Tonbridge and Edenbridge was badly flooded in October 1987 after days of persistent rain. The giant barrier, however, proved to be a worthy investment. It held back the water and certainly saved the two towns from serious flooding. On this occasion many parts of Kent were on a Grade One flood alert.

No More Floods in Tonbridge?

IN a determined and costly effort to save Tonbridge, Maidstone, Edenbridge and scores of villages, hamlets and farmland from more chaos and misery, the River Medway Flood Relief Act was introduced in 1976. It gave the signal for work to commence on a giant flood storage reservoir where the rivers Medway and Eden meet, south of Tonbridge.

The reservoir was created by building an earthen flood barrier some 300 metres long and, in places as much as 5.7 metres high, across the Medway valley. This holds back surplus water which can be released at a rate sufficient to prevent flooding lower down the river through a control structure in the barrier.

This contains a modern sluice, with three radial gates, which releases water into a new channel. The old river bed is thus by-passed. The work was commissioned in 1981 at a cost of £3.6million and completed a few years later. The engineers were satisfied that there would be no repetition of the floods of 1900, 1909, 1935, 1947, 1960 and 1968. Will they be successful?

Wake of 'The Hurricane'

16th October, 1987

WHAT an extraordinary year 1987 was proving to be. Heavy rain, floods, blizzards, snow-drifts and gale force winds had hit the county. As the damp autumn progressed, many wondered if Mother Nature had any more tricks up her sleeve. The answer came in the dark, early hours of Friday 16th October. As an unsuspecting county slept, a storm - destined to be the most destructive of the century - was brewing in the English Channel.

West and South Kent were the first to discover that all was not well. Soon after midnight dustbin lids clashed like cymbals against the ground and then cartwheeled down the road. By daybreak the whole of the county was reeling from a storm which had devastated homes, torn up trees by the million, crushed hundreds of cars, crippled communications, changed the face of the landscape and moved on to dislocate London and the eastern counties.

It all happened in a few hours. There had been nothing exceptional about the weather forecast for the night. Storm winds were reported to be sweeping across the Atlantic but they were going to miss Britain. At 1 am the winds hit the Kent coast. Within five hours lorries and aircraft were overturned, entire roofs and walls sucked from houses. Homes were plunged into darkness as electricity supplies failed and telephone wires were pulled down.

The power of the wind, which in places exceeded 100 miles an hour, felled an estimated 15 million trees in the South East and its ferocity left 19 people dead. For a long time, in bewildered communities, life came to almost a standstill and then developed a new slow pace of candlelit meals without television or telephone. Statistics abounded as the final cost was evaluated at £1 billion. Today, the Great Storm, or so-called Hurricane, of 1987 has passed into folklore, widely accepted in most of southern England as the meteorological event of the century.

No-one had known what was about to happen. On Thursday 15th October, the computer in the Met. Office at Bracknell showed a moderate but deepening depression with a centre of 970 millibars just to the south of Cape Finisterre. The data and the lack of weatherships made it difficult to ascertain how fast it would deepen and which way it would go. There was no doubt that exceptionally strong winds would be coming across France, Belgium, Holland and The Channel but in Britain there was no such certainty. In Kent, along the river valleys and throughout the Weald, council workers, police and firemen were more concerned about the possibility of further flooding. Following the torrents of rain which had fallen during the previous days, the county was, once again, on a Grade One flood alert.

By 2 am the wind speed in Kent was in excess of 40 mph and the centre of the low pressure area was near Bristol. Exceptionally cold air plunging south over the Atlantic had combined with warm air drawn up from sub-tropical latitudes. On meeting the jet stream the depression was explosively deepened to produce a catastrophic force of turbulence and destructiveness. At first it seemed that the tempest would pass up the Channel, as forecast, but the low point took an unexpected turn to the north and the wind veered across the centre of southern England.

In Folkestone, the cross-Channel ferry Hengist was safely tied up in port, secured for storm conditions at 24 points. As the waves, whipped up by the ever-increasing speed of the wind, started to batter the ship, she broke her moorings one by one. Each mooring was replaced by the crew but, with a continuous wall of water sweeping over the ship, the master decided to start the engines and put to sea. The harbour was far too dangerous.

The sea was rolling violently, so much in fact that the engines of the Hengist tripped out and the propellers lifted out of the water. She was then plunged into darkness and rolled helplessly with the captain, Sid Bridgewater, and 24 crew members fearing she would soon turn turtle. At 5 am she was blown onto the Warren, where she stayed firmly aground.

A few miles up the Kent coast, Folkestone's busier neighbour, Dover, was having problems of its own. Newspapers reported that the harbour had to be closed for the first time in living memory but harbour officials denied that was the case, insisting that it would have been contrary to all traditions of the sea to have turned any vessel away in the prevailing conditions.

One ship at sea was the 8,000 ton Sealink vessel St Christopher which lay all night off Dover, with passengers on board, waiting for the winds to moderate. They didn't. Waves, 40 feet high, buckled the steel doors of the upper car deck and the ship rolled so much that three lorries toppled over and slithered to and fro crushing many cars. To the relief of the passengers, St Christopher, the patron saint of travel, was looking after them. The ship finally docked at 2 pm the following afternoon.

At 6.45 am the small coaster Sumnia tried to enter Dover Harbour. She had been sheltering in the lea of Dungeness and had dragged her anchors. She sent a Mayday call at 5 am and made a run for Dover. As she tried to turn the corner into port, she was blown onto the breakwater and suddenly tipped over. Into those murderous seas went the Dover Lifeboat, commanded by acting coxswain Roy Couzens. They took two men off the coaster's bow and a port tug rescued another

This is the Hengist, swept onto a concrete apron at Folkestone Warren by raging seas and hurricane-force winds.

before a wave engulfed the wrecked ship. On the way back they rescued a fourth member of the crew who was in the water holding on to a lifejacket. There was no sign of the remaining two mariners. One was discovered a day later on top of the breakwater. The other, the master of the Sumnia, was swept away to sea.

In east and south Kent the wind reached speeds of 80 miles an hour and more. It tore through streets, thumping on windows and kicking at doors. It hoisted roofs in the air and buffetted walls and chimneys sending them crashing to the ground. At Capel, on top of the cliffs, a caravan park was totally demolished; in Folkestone, schools and churches were damaged; in Hythe the roof of the swimming pool was lifted off; in Sandgate, roads were swamped as waves came over the promenade; at Port Lympne, zookeepers mounted a round-the-clock vigil to comfort the animals and prevent escape.

In Howletts Zoo, Canterbury, one animal did escape during the height of the storm. Xiang, a seven-year-old clouded leopard roamed free in the area for seven days.

Eventually, hungry and bedraggled, he was baited back with dead chicken and re-united with his keeper.

As trees fell, some individually, some in ranks and some, one after the other, like dominoes, people in Kent thought they were the victims of a freak whirlwind that had escaped other areas. The morning revealed the truth.

At Chilham Castle a 300-yard double avenue of 150 year-old limes fell within three minutes of each other without a single survivor. At Knole Park, Sevenoaks, hundreds of trees that had withstood gales for 400 years or more, were uprooted. At Bedgebury Forest, Goudhurst, 5,500 acres of woodland, the equivalent of 10 years of harvesting, were destroyed. All over Kent, great trees in full leaf caught the wind like the sails of tea clippers; the ground was sodden after many days of rain, their roots were not restrained and they toppled like ninepins.

On this wild night the Weald of Kent was devastated. In the finest parks and gardens, mature woodlands and orchards, centuries of careful management, were destroyed in little more than two hours. And there were three fatalities in the county, all victims of

Glasshouses all over Kent were shattered. This one at Headcorn covered one third of an acre and left the family with a £250,000 bill and the task of clearing up 18 tons of glass.

falling trees.

The hurricane-force wind bulldozed its relentless course across every National Trust Garden in Kent - Scotney, Emmetts, Sissinghurst, Ightham Mote, Knole and Chartwell, where Winston Churchill used to look across the lakes to his woods. Villages on the Greensand Ridge and the North Downs were cut off by fallen trees and cables. The town of Sevenoaks, also isolated, lost its name when six of the famous oaks, planted in 1902 to commemorate the coronation of Edward Vll, toppled over. Such was the magnitude of this storm that almost every person in Kent had a story to tell. The days that followed this storm were not idle ones. Electricity workers had the massive task of re-erecting the huge pylons and re-connecting miles and miles of overhead cables. Much of Kent had been plunged into darkness at the height of the storm and many homes had no electricity for several days. In some remote villages and isolated farms it was a week or more before householders could dispense with Tilly lamps and makeshift meals cooked over an open fire. Helicopters were brought in to locate the faults and engineers and linesmen were drafted in from all over England. They were backed up by soldiers from the Royal Engineers and the Gurkha Rifle Regiment, based at Chatham, who brought their famous fighting qualities and jungle warfare to the more remote areas of Kent.

There had been nothing to compare with the cost of the 1987 storm in Britain in modern times. The Association of British Insurers estimated that approximately one insured household in six in southern England suffered substantial damage. More than 1.2 million claims were received. In comparable terms the great tidal surge of 1953 caused insured losses of about £400 million - but this excluded the cost of improving sea defences.

If there were to be a pecking order among Kentish storms this century, the hurricane-force winds of 16th October, 1987, would probably come second to the tidal surge of 1953. Both will be major talking points well into the next century and possibly beyond. After all, storms of this magnitude, according to the law of averages, were unlikely to occur again for at least 250 years.

Less than three years were to lapse before Mother Nature again made mockery of the laws of averages.

A room with a view - this view. Ironically the house where the film was made, Foxwold, Brasted Chart, probably had its view more radically altered than any other home in the country. Parts of Brasted Chart, Ide Hill and Toys Hill - where almost 400 acres of National Trust woodland were destroyed - remained isolated from the outside world for many days. Also cut off, and without supplies, were the handicapped residents of Care Village, a home set deep in the woods. Eventually a man climbed out of a pile of fallen foliage and said: "Hello, I'm from the district council. Are you all right!" They were liberated by the army.

The battle to restore power and telephone lines began as soon as the first desperate messages came into electricity and Telecom offices in dozens of towns. Local crews were joined by repair teams from all over England, Scotland and Wales who were shocked by the sight of overhead lines in tangled coils across hundreds of miles of Kentish lanes. It took at least two weeks to re-connect power to every home and the cost of that operation alone in West Kent amounted to £530,000.

147

A wooden cross was carried from St Justus, Rochester. The church was felled by the villainous winds.

The Community Hall at Wye was reduced to a pile of rubble.

On the 16th October 1987. A Hurricane Destroyed
Six of The Seven Oak Trees
Planted here in the Year 1902 .
On the 6th December 1987
The Ceremony of Replacement Planting
was conducted by
THE TREES FOR THE FUTURE APPEAL
To Commemorate this Occasion A Time Capsule
Containing Documentation of the Disaster
Has been buried in these grounds.

Early in December, 1987, the town of Sevenoaks held a fair on the Vine Cricket Ground to celebrate the planting of seven young sessile oaks to replace those blown down in the storm. It was called a "hurricane fayre". Some 15,000 people turned up and local television celebrities took turns in symbolically planting the new oaks. A year later, on the anniversary of the storm, another ceremony was held to bury, beneath a marble plaque, a "time warp" containing memorabilia of the historic day Sevenoaks "lost its name". When guests arrived they discovered, to their horror, that the sapling oaks had been savaged by vandals.

Every little tree was snapped in half. Within weeks a third ceremony was held, beneath the sturdy branches of the one oak to resist the wind and, on this occasion, seven slightly larger and stronger oaks were planted. Today, King Oak, as the survivor is known, stands sentinel among the seven smaller oaks and welcomes visitors from all over the world. The story is featured in an illustrated book for children called King Oak of Sevenoaks.

June, 1989 brought a temporary cooling of the weather and on 6th June the Hempstead Valley, Gillingham had a six inch covering of ice. There was considerable debate as to whether it was snow or hail, with disagreement even among meteorologists. Hail won the day.

A Decade to Remember

1980: On 5th September a tornado ripped through Smarden at around noon with damage to roofs, trees and fencing. At Vesper Hawk Farm it was the second time that it had been struck by such a storm. On 2nd January, 1966 a gander had been killed by flying debris.

1981: A series of tornadoes swept across Kent on 20th October. At High Halden, near Ashford, trees were uprooted and carried over a hedge, greenhouses were shattered and a shed was blown across two fields. Water from a pond was siphoned out by the vortex. There was exceptional cold in December.

1982: During a cold spell in mid-January, Orpington and Sevenoaks recorded 10F (-14C) and the ground was covered with snow for more than a week.

1983: Dover ground to a halt on 9th-10th February as 14 inches of snow fell. Bus services were suspended and pupils sent home from school. Further snow carpeted the ground on Easter Sunday.

July over England as a whole was the warmest since records were first devised in 1659, with an average value above 68F (20C) over most of Kent. On 16th July Gillingham recorded 91F (33C).

1984: The western half of Kent in particular felt the effects of ex-hurricane "Hortense" on 5th October. Having travelled from near Bermuda it brought a day of heavy rain and thunder. At Shortlands near Bromley 1.6 inches or 41mm of rain fell.

1985: The sea froze at Pegwell Bay, near Ramsgate, in February. Christmas, 1985 brought high winds and rain. At Jubilee Corner 2.2 inches (55mm) of rain fell with extensive flooding in the Stour Valley. In south Ashford this caused £50,000 worth of damage. The wind gusted to 72 mph at Langdon Bay.

1988: Showers of rain, sleet and snow were accompanied by a waterspout at Dover on 21st November and snow lay for five days.

The Garden of England Wilts

1989-1991

THE burning years of 1989 and 1990 were to bring the issue of global warming to the forefront, not only among scientists but as everyday conversation throughout Britain. For Kent they were reminiscent of 1976 with records for continuous sunshine, tinder dry countryside, heat-related fatalities and water restrictions everywhere.

1989 began with exceptionally mild weather and by April spring plants were flowering several weeks early. The dry spell continued into May, a remarkable month with no rain at all in parts of Tunbridge Wells and an average of more than 10 hours of daily sunshine. At East Malling it was the sunniest of any month since 1914. By now underground water supplies were many metres below normal as was the reservoir at Bewl Water. Demand was 30 per cent higher than in 1976 and hosepipe bans were quickly introduced to many parts of the county.

After a major June hailstorm at Hempstead Valley, Gillingham, blue skies and hot sunshine returned in July and 91F (33C) was recorded at Hadlow. Trees began to shed their leaves and by September, Kent was again in need of prolonged rainfall. Although thundery conditions developed, some areas received a deluge while others remained dry. Violent storms reverberated over Gillingham on 12th July and brought the equivalent of a month's rainfall in just four hours. A branch of Barclays Bank and the Guildhall Museum in Rochester were struck by lightning while Faversham lost most of its power supplies.

Burglar alarms were activated by electrical surges and ironically, in the face of the drought, flood-waters cascaded down the A26 between Tonbridge and Maidstone and on the A20 at Harrietsham Bridge. The rains, however, did little to alleviate the dwindling groundwater supplies.

Autumn brought no large quantities of rain. The latter half of November and the beginning of December brought an almost unprecedented dry spell but the calm was not to last. Eighty-mile-an-hour winds trapped six cross-Channel ferries outside the harbour at Dover and a boy was swept away by a giant wave at Folkestone. The year ended violently but Kent had experienced its third sunniest year on record, behind 1959 and 1949.

There was no respite in 1990. Every week in January and February the weather grabbed the headlines, with the storm of 25th January, in some areas, surpassing the fury of October 1987.

The winter was so warm that some dormant plants came into bloom and for most of the county temperatures exceeded all known records. Winter in Kent in 1990 was more akin to that of the Mediterranean with warm weather and gales. Although 14 inches (370mm) fell during the winter, the deficit of ground water had not been made up. Concern heightened when blue skies and blazing sunshine on the 23rd February sent the mercury to the almost summery temperature of 64F (18C). Then March gave only three days of rain.

By early April, Bewl Water, which augments the Medway's flow, was only 70 per cent full and, after a blazing weekend on 5th and 6th May, hosepipe bans were introduced for 170,000 homes from Gravesend to Sheppey. Following the driest May on record in parts of Kent the restrictions were extended to Thanet, Sandwich and Deal.

July 1990 was almost entirely dominated by a vast area of descending dry air, an anticyclone, which dried out the soil's moisture from the June rains and gave a reading of 88F (31C) to Orpington on 22nd July. It continued into August and the stage was set for the sensational day on the 3rd when the British record temperature of 98F (36.7C), previously held by Canterbury, was beaten by Cheltenham with 99F (37C). In Kent during this August week the temperature soared to 97F. It brought a most unusual problem. Ashford's environmental officers warned of exploding compost heaps as gasses from within were spontaneously igniting in the heat.

Tragically two young men were drowned at Horton Kirby, near Swanley when they plunged into a lake to cool off and a fireman died at Tiffenden, High Halden in a blazing cornfield. Throughout the county, still littered with fallen trees from the 1987 and 1990 storms, flames spread with alarming speed and fire fighting resources were again severely depleted.

It was no surprise that further restrictions to the water supply were announced. Southern Water introduced draconian measures. No watering by hoses and sprinklers in gardens or racecourses, no filling of privately-owned swimming pools, no washing the exterior of buildings or ornamental fountains. Kent waited for the autumn rains but some parts received an earlier soaking. Heavy thunderstorms blacked out a concert at Leeds Castle, lightning struck a house at Ditton and there was flash flooding at Folkestone. Autumn brought rain but not enough.

1990 had been the warmest and sunniest year in Kent's weather history.

Three long summers of drought took a heavy toll on the River Darent. Cracked mud at Horton-Kirby (above) typified the dry river bed as did stranded fish flopping uselessly in fingernail deep puddles.

Kent's Highs and Lows

HOTTEST DAY
THE highest official temperature ever attained in Kent was on 9th August, 1911 at Canterbury when the thermometer soared to 98F (36.7C). This remained a national record until 1990 when Cheltenham recorded 99F (37.1C).

COLDEST DAY
The coldest reading in Kent was recorded in the bitter February of 1947 when the temperature in Elmstone, between Canterbury and Sandwich, plunged to -6F (-21.1C). A reading of -10F at East Peckham on 5th January, 1867 is often quoted.

WETTEST DAY
The wettest day in Kent was at West Stourmouth on 20th September, 1973 with 7.51 inches (187.75mm), or nearly four times the monthly average. Mention must be made of the severe storm which gave 5.14 inches (131mm) in just two hours at Knockholt, the second largest fall in such a short time known in Britain.

COLDEST WINTER
The coldest winter in Kent was 1683-4 when persistent northerly winds swept polar ice south down the North Sea forcing it through the Dover Straits. The sea ports were closed for some days and an observer spoke of thick ice moving fast westwards driven by wind and current.

DRIEST YEAR
The driest year in Kent was 1921 when Margate recorded only 9.29 inches (236mm) of rain. Several months have seen no rain at all, for instance February, 1959 at Herne Bay, June, 1976 at Biddenden and June, 1989 in Thanet.

SUNNIEST YEAR
The year 1990 goes down in history as the sunniest and warmest the county has experienced. Some coastal locations had more than 2,000 hours of sunshine.

And It Happened Again!

25th January 1990

THE gale of 25th January, 1990 left more people dead in Britain than any other single weather-related event since the East Coast flood disaster in 1953. Of the 47 deaths, 36 were a direct result of the storm.

The high number of fatalities was attributed to the fact that the storm struck during the day when more people were out and about. If the 1987 storm had occurred during daylight hours no doubt the figures would have been gravely higher. The 1990 tempest also affected a larger area of the country. In Kent, a woman died when a tree toppled on a florist's van in East Street, Hunton, near Maidstone.

The Atlantic depression responsible had deepened explosively as it travelled in from the east coast of North America. This time, unlike in 1987, the Met Office had given adequate warnings on television. At Dover the gusts reached hurricane force, touching 104 mph, and it is estimated that winds exceeded 100 mph in many hilly and open places in the South East.

Again thousands of trees were felled in Kent and countless roads were blocked. Homes were blacked out and phone lines severed. Across Britain some four million trees were uprooted. This compared to 15 million in South East England in October 1987.

In January at least six depressions reached the very low pressure reading of 950 mbs (28.01 ins) over the Atlantic. This is believed to have been partly caused by below average temperatures in the Greenland and Iceland area, combined with the effects of above average readings in Northern Europe, causing a marked gradient.

Worst hit of the North Kent schools was the Fort Luton which was partly closed for several weeks. In Rochester, the Foster family living opposite St Margaret's Church were terrified by a bombardment of heavy slates ripped from the church roof, slamming through the front windows of the house.

In and around Ashford there were scenes reminiscent of the October 1987 storm. More than 1,400 buildings owned by the local council were damaged. Families in Wye held their breath after a large chimney toppled over at the King's Head Hotel and balanced itself precariously above picturesque Church Street in the village. In 1987 the hotel's chimney crashed down through to the butcher's shop roof and almost destroyed two cars. Villagers feared a repitition. For the second time in two and a half years, Kent County Nursery at Challock was devastated.

The storm coincided with a national ambulance dispute but striking ambulancemen refused pay and answered 999 calls during the crisis after an appeal on Radio Kent. Across the county, calls to the police and fire service came in at the rate of 100 an hour. An Ashford police spokesman said: "It was absolute chaos. We didn't know what was going to happen next."

The tallest building in Maidstone, nine storey Colman House in King Streeet, was evacuated after occupants claimed it was swaying. An office worker said it was, "like being in an earthquake". Winds were so strong that pedestrians had to cling on to lamp posts to stay upright.

Razor sharp roof panels posed a danger on the A20 at Bearsted when they became airborne and police were called in to "arrest" them. British Telecom workers struggled day and night to repair the 6,500 faults in the Mid Kent and Weald areas alone.

Nationally, the storm - together with other damaging gales in February 1990 - cost insurance companies £2,081 million, compared with £1,227 million after the 1987 hurricane. The big freeze figure for January 1987 was put at £332 million and the cold spell of 1981-2, £383 million.

The storm of 1990 provided many spectacular sights including the surprise visit of a fin whale whose navigational ability was undermined by the churning seas. It came ashore at New Romney.

Lorry drivers who attempted to cross the great expanse of the M2 motorway bridge at Rochester during the gale of 25th January, 1990 had an unpleasant surprise. Every lorry was blown off course and at least six toppled onto their sides.

Mayhem at Hythe

25th-28th February, 1990

Although it was the mildest January and February on record this was no consolation to the residents adjacent to the promenade at Hythe. An unfortunate combination of severe gales and high spring tides led to mountainous seas which smashed sea defences and flooded homes.

With sea temperatures in mid Atlantic remaining above average and cold arctic air flooding south to meet it the ingredients were there for a rapid deepening of air pressure and strong winds. A seemingly endless run of such systems battered Britain. On the 7th winds reached 90 mph at Sheerness, but it was those on the 25th to the 26th that really brought serious problems.

The whole of the south-east Kent coastline was affected with Hythe taking the worst of the pounding. Waves crashed over the promenade, dwarfing the nearby houses and filling some of their ground floor rooms with tons of shingle. One man was trapped by his arm as he tried to flee his home when flood water crushed the door against him. Rescuers managed to free him by battering down the door with a sledge hammer. Damage was particularly severe between Ormonde Road eastwards to the Marine Parade. Altogether some 250 feet of promenade and 35 feet of sea wall were ripped away.

Immediate repairs to the crumbling sea wall were carried out in frenzied haste as the next high tides threatened further devastation. Contractors poured cement into the breaches before the sea flooded back and the pounding began again in earnest. At Sandgate about 250 feet of shingle-covered foreshore was reduced to just 30 feet by the scouring effect of the waves.

By early March the storms abated and the work of reconstruction could start. It took three months concentrated efforts at a cost of half a million pounds to complete but a major scheme has been proposed for the future.

Roy Plowright, a keen gardener, semi-retired from the chemistry department of Kent University at Canterbury, pictured here digging for victory.

Man of Kent Digging for Victory

AS the hosepipe ban moved into a record third consecutive summer, horticulturists in the Garden of England began to talk even more seriously about global warming and the greenhouse effect, for they were now experiencing the most prolonged drought of the century.

By the end of May, 1991 - which over England as a whole was the driest since 1893 - the county was so parched that rivers had shrunk, reservoirs were drying up and the 525,000 consumers of the Mid Kent Water Company were still labouring under orders which forbade the use of sprinklers and hosepipes. The company even commissioned Kent Agricultural College at Wye to research which plants grew best in dry conditions so they could pass on advice to gardeners.

Many people resorted to illegal but surreptitious midnight watering by trailing yards of hosepipe over rooftops. Others fixed up ingenious devices for using the bath-water. Some built huge tanks under patios to collect what winter rainfall they could. Roy Plowright of Canterbury created his own well. He enjoyed the challenge. "It took me back to the days of self sufficiency", he said. "I dug a bore three feet deep in 1990 and the following year went down a further five feet. I knew of the presence of water as Monk's Well is only a short distance away."

June's heavy rainfalls brought a fragrant freshness to the countryside that had been missing for two summers but the water companies still believed the only answer for a county so heavily dependent on ground water sources tapped through boreholes was more reservoirs. Mid Kent and Southern Water plan to build one at Broad Oak, Canterbury and this, combined with the first direct abstraction of the River Medway at Yalding, should meet further needs.

Canterbury's great survivor

THIS photograph was taken in the winter of 1991 from "Bell Harry", the 250-foot pinnacle of Canterbury Cathedral. Below are the richly ornate twin towers and snow-covered rooftops of this ageless Kentish city which has been a centre of Christian pilgrimage for hundreds of years.

Canterbury Cathedral, the mother church of England, grew from a monastery established by St Augustine in 602, five years after he first arrived in Kent, and is the country's greatest survivor. From her lofty position she has seen the shrinkage of the Wantsum Channel and welcomed the Isle of Thanet to mainland Kent. She has withstood whirlwinds and tornadoes, great storms and gales of hurricane force.

Thunder has frequently boomed around her and she has been majestically silhouetted by flashes of lightning. Below she has seen the swirling flood waters of the River Stour lap the ancient streets and blizzards sweep across the countryside leaving great drifts in the exposed marshlands to the north. Only once, during the earthquake of 1382, when the Bell Tower was destroyed, did the Cathedral show her vulnerability.

The works of our forefathers have survived not only time and weather but schism, rebellion, bombs and fire. The living heritage of 1,400 years and the faith in which it was established is here in this historic Cathedral — a sentinel for Kent which will continue to endure the elements for hundreds, perhaps thousands, of years to come.

Oh dear, too much water...

THERE is no subject on which the British people have a shorter memory than the weather. After five years of below-average rainfall with hosepipe bans, dried up reservoirs and bare earth in place of grass suddenly everyone was grumbling about...the rain.

Perhaps they had good reason. During September and October 1993 there were days when it poured with almost tropical intensity and it was the wettest December in Dover since 1959 with 190.4mm. All over the county, rivers burst their banks and traffic was diverted from flooded roads. It was the same story in January 1994 — the month that Chichester in West Sussex went Venetian, freezers were seen floating down Uckfield High Street and a landslip in Haywards Heath caused 14 homes to be demolished.

The winter of 1993-94 was not only extremely wet but also one of the mildest. In fact soil temperatures in early December were similar to those of early May.

Another watery occasion occurred in February 1995, when the ford outside Bekesbourne church was flooded to a depth of almost two feet. Bride Penny Hill found her way blocked until a Brett's lorry saved the day and took her in the bridal car across the water to meet her groom Martin Harman in the nick of time.

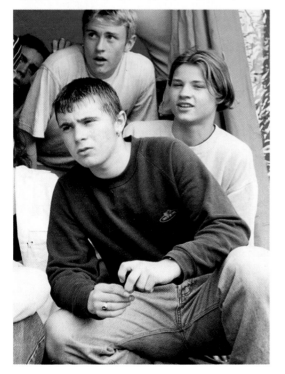

Bolt from the heavens strikes boy in tent

A hot spell in July 1994, which saw temperatures reach 90F (32C) in many parts of inland Kent, was followed by the inevitable thunderstorms in July and August.

Prolonged and vivid flashes of lightning were also seen in September — a month which a group of schoolfriends will never forget. As they were enjoying a night together under canvas, at Rusthall, near Tunbridge Wells, before the start of the new term, a bolt of lightning hit the tent and went straight through the body of 15-year-old Stefan Brown (front of picture). He was seriously burned, unconscious, but alive.

As Stefan and his friends recovered in hospital, storms continued to batter Kent leaving hundreds of homes under water.

Now there's too much sun...

AUGUST 1995 was memorable — the hottest August of the century, a month of barbecues and blazes, of extended pub hours, cloudless skies and overheated cars. Firemen were busy. So were the nudist beaches. Roads were jammed. Caravans overturned as their tyres blew out.

In town centres people jumped into ponds and fountains to keep cool, a windsurfer was seen naked near Hythe. Cabriolet sales soared in Folkestone and the whiff of coconut suntan oil pervaded Thanet beaches.

The summer got off to a blistering start in May when temperatures soared into the low 80s F but early June was cool. It became warmer as the month progressed and July was very warm — over 70F (21C) at midnight in Westerham on the 21st. But August was the month to remember. At Postling, near Hythe, 33.2C (91F) was recorded on 1st with 25C (77F) at 2am on the following night.

As holidaymakers headed for the beaches, doctors renewed their warnings about the danger of too much sun. This followed the discovery of the body of a bather at Fairlight, East Sussex. Dressed only in shorts, Steven Flack's upper body and legs were severely burned — a grim reminder of the sun's power.

Once again Kent paid the price of the heatwave as hosepipe bans came into effect. Part of the problem was leaks. Southern Water admitted they were losing nearly 20 million gallons every day, across their area despite almost halving the amount lost daily, since privatisation.

Mike Setford from Mid Kent Water said: "There isn't a shortage of water, just a lack of pumping facilities to meet the increased demand which is 40 per cent higher than normal."

The people of Dover love a good excuse for a party and the splendid weather in early May provided one. Or was it the fact that this week was the 50th anniversary of VE Day and a national holiday was declared? Anyway it was shirt-sleeve order in Priory Grove — just one of many sun-blessed street parties all over the country.

Overheated motorists are blown out to sea!

Another phenomena attributed to the exceptionally hot month of August 1995 was the heated motorist. Road rage became such an epidemic that the Rev. Howard Daubney of Rochester set up a set of guidelines to help drivers defuse the situation. Don't worry about the weather, he said, but lock the doors and windows, stay in your car and avoid eye contact when confronted by one of these hot-headed road hogs.

Trouble on the road and trouble at sea. The RNLI reported its busiest ever month in Kent with double the number of calls. "People drive to the coast from London", said a spokesman, "and they're hot. So they sit on their inflatables, get blown out to sea and we have to rescue them."

Lightning strike left holes in toes

SEPTEMBER 1995. Seventeen people, sheltering under a tree at Aylesford when rain interrupted a schoolboy football match, were hit by a single lightning strike. All survived although, with severe injuries ranging from cardiac arrest to ear drum rupture, some were in intensive care for many weeks. Ten of those hit discovered that small holes had been burned into the tips of their shoes.

The previously unknown pattern of injury, was caused as the electricity from the lightning left their body. The holes were about the size of a match-head and one appeared on each toe and at one inch intervals around the soles.

The injuries were examined by plastic surgeon, Mr Fahmy Saas Fahmy, then registrar in plastic surgery at the burns unit in St Andrews Hospital, Billericay.

Jackie Hunt of Penenden Heath, Maidstone was one of the victims. She said the marks were like round dots, darker in the centre, on the tips of toes and round the sides of the feet. They were deep and painful.

Doctors believe the injuries may lead to a better understanding of how electrical discharges affect the body and are naming the phenomenon "tip-toe" signs.

MAY 30th 1995. A particularly active thunderstorm covering a few square miles on the Downs between Canterbury, Ashford and Hythe produced marble-sized (16mm) diameter hailstones which accumulated to depths of 6 inches, in the parish of Elmsted. The photograph, contributed by Mr Jerome Bennett, shows an igloo formation beside Elmsted Church having an ice depth of 19 inches. There were also drifts of 1-2 feet in the lanes north of the village. The previous day, Whitsun Bank Holiday Monday, had been brilliantly sunny with teas served outside the church.

Vehicles abandoned in M25 treachery

December 5th 1995

HUNDREDS of motorists left their cars on the Kent stretch of the M25 as treacherous conditions made driving impossible. Drivers described it as "Hell on the M25", after spending 5 hours covering 3 miles. Some attempted to walk home, others made their way gingerly to the Clackett Lane Service Station, near Westerham, where they stayed for the night.

By 1.00 am on Wednesday December 6th there were more than 1,000 people sleeping on floors while the traffic queue, paralysed by the abandoned vehicles, stretched both west and east for several miles.

Manager of the service station Peter Whitlock said: "These are the worst conditions I have ever seen on a motorway. There were more than 1,000 people here and we had to put mothers with young babies in offices and training rooms for the night."

The nightmare continued the next morning with motorists trying to locate their vehicles and then make their way to home or office.

As schools closed and postmen and police struggled to get to stations and sorting offices came the prediction for a white Christmas. Weather experts were pointing out that an easterly pattern had become established and there could well be the first classic Christmas white-out since 1970.

Several hundred people throughout Kent rushed to the betting shops but they were disappointed. It was cold with temperatures around freezing but the snow did not arrive in Kent until Boxing Day evening. Sub zero temperatures and atrocious conditions returned on the last Saturday of the year with a vengeance. Once again we had that rarest of weather events — freezing rain followed by glaze.

Scores of people were treated after falling on clear ice which had coated the surfaces of footpaths, driveways and even shopping centres and some places reported that "walking was impossible". Driving, however, was not too difficult. On this occasion the motorway had been gritted.

It was hard work cycling through the flood water in Folkestone on August 11th, 1996. When the mopping up had been completed, inhabitants accused the Shepway council and Southern Water of incompetence. They said the beach nourishment scheme in Sandgate blocked storm drain outfalls causing thousands of pounds of damage. A Shepway spokesman said it was just a freak situation. "The drains are Victorian, similar to those in other towns and nothing could have stopped the flood". During the emergency Kent Fire Brigade received an incredible 618 calls for help.

Black Bull Road, Folkestone where the water reached eight feet in places.

People rescued in dinghies as flash floods hit Folkestone

August 11th, 1996

FLASH floods, described at the time as being "of biblical proportions", swirled through Folkestone and district following one of the worst storms of the century. In two hours almost four inches of rain (100 mm) fell and caused a deluge that proved too much for the drains to handle. Within minutes the pressure of the water left several homes with major structural damage and on the point of collapse.

Elsewhere there were scenes of chaos and destruction with businesses and homes flooded and cars carried away by the fast-flowing waters.

Central Folkestone was the worst affected. Water levels reached eight feet in places, completely covering front doors. The only way people could be rescued from their homes was by means of dinghies delivered by the rescue services to first-floor windows.

There were several dramatic moments. At one point quick-thinking fishermen smashed down a harbour wall in a bid to direct rising flood water into the sea. With an emergency call coming into the brigade headquarters every 25 seconds, firemen were in the thick of the action helping to take six people to hospital with minor injuries. The emergency services said it was sheer luck that no-one was more seriously hurt.

The Queen Mother, as Lord Warden of the Cinque Ports, sent a message of sympathy to the families whose homes had been damaged and Michael Howard, MP for Shepway, said he would set an appeal fund rolling with an undisclosed donation.

The Mayor of Folkestone, Councillor Roz Everett, urged all inhabitants to give cash to the fund instead of giving to the lottery. She was stranded in her home in Pavilion Road and said the sight of the water rising so quickly was frightening. "I have never known anything like it before", she said.

As is often the case with such disasters a heartwarming community spirit shone through. In one touching scene elderly residents from Bradford Court Sheltered Homes cooked hot meals and cared for seven pensioners who had been left homeless.

In those two destructive hours more than double the usual amount of rain for the whole of August fell. Southern Water spokesman Mary McCabe said: "Drains were bursting due to the extreme intensity of the water and the Pent stream broke its banks. Rain and foul-water sewers could not cope."

This photograph shows the remains of a 120-foot giant redwood tree which exploded after being struck by lightning on the afternoon of Wednesday August 28th 1996 — a most unusual weather phenomenon. The tree, in a garden at Bayley's Hill, Sevenoaks, came crashing to the ground narrowly missing the house full of people and the gardener at work. Branches were found 250 yards away in neighbouring gardens and a car parked outside was written off by flying shards of wood which also made great holes in the roof of the house. The lightning strike came almost without warning and was not followed by any kind of rain or storm. The owner of the house said there was a huge bang and she rushed outside. Some seconds later branches began to fall from the sky indicating the height they had reached. No-one was hurt.

The wintry blast of January 1997 provided East Kent newspapers with some traditional stories and some more unusual including one in which police at Folkestone caught a burglar by following his footprints in the snow!

East Kent's biting wind claims a life

January 3rd, 1997

A JANUARY without snow is like a summer without the song thrush or the smell of freshly cut hay. By the end of 1996, after nine nearly snowless Januaries, snow lovers were beginning to despair of seeing one of those traditional Kentish January blizzards, when there is chaos on road and rail and downland villages enjoy a few days of splendid isolation. The infamous January of 1987 was just a distant memory.

They need not have worried. The first day of the year brought snow at last, although it was only to towns and villages east of Maidstone. Ten centimetres fell and caught so many councils by surprise that scores of drivers found themselves skidding out of control on untreated roads. In Canterbury it was so cold that shops closed early.

The snow did not last but the cold weather claimed a victim when a man froze to death just a few yards from his front door after a night out drinking. Police said that Antony Keeble, 29, had tried to walk to his home at Gibbins Brook, Sellindge, without a warm coat. With temperatures plummeting to -6C (21F), hypothermia set in and it is believed the alcohol stripped away his resistance and left him feeling disorientated. He was found in a neighbour's garden 30 hours later after a frantic search by helicopter.

Mr Keeble had tried in vain to find shelter from the biting winds and arctic conditions by crawling into a chicken coop in his neighbour's garden.

April and May blow hot and bitter cold

When the earth tilts sufficiently to encourage the buds to open and a maiden can stand on seven daisies at once and warm, showery weather is common, it means that April has arrived.

April 1997, however, was not the norm. It rained very little in Kent, temperatures soared into the seventies, the London Weather Centre warned that the first four months of 1997, countrywide were the driest for 68 years and the Environment Agency urged the water supply industry to impose hosepipe bans immediately.

In fact by the end of April 1997 the Institute of Hydrology was saying that underground water levels were already the same as in 1976. To add to the woes of those who live off the countryside came a frost, on April 21st, so devastating that leaves, flowers and young buds turned brown in the orchards. North and mid-Kent fruit farmers were inconsolable, claiming their businesses had been ruined. It certainly was an April to remember (or forget).

So May arrived with the knowledge that 45 days had passed without a major downpour and Kent had experienced the driest three-month period from March to May, since 1976.

Water levels as low as 1976. Illustrated by these children cycling in the dried up bed of the River Dour in Russell Gardens, Dover in the autumn of 1996.

Then, on May 5th, came the cruellest twist of all — another frost so severe that wisteria (see back cover picture) young shoots and even early bracken died. The cuckoo must have wondered what on earth he was doing in this wintry climate. The cold was followed by a dusty easterly wind and overcast skies.

One of the wettest Junes — but drought goes on

THE driest January, the sunniest April, the coldest May. As the weather records tumbled, meteorologists predicted that June would be wet. They were right. June 1997 hit the high water mark — one of the wettest of the century.

Average rainfall in Kent over the 30 days was 133.7 millimetres, nearly double the 70mm recorded during the entire summer of 1995 and a stark contrast to June 1996 when just 30 mm fell.

Inevitably there was a price to pay. The rain squalls, which came with so much rapidity, swept away hundreds of seabirds from their breeding sites on the Kent coast. Further north, at Bempton in Northumberland, the RSPB estimated that up to 150,000 birds were killed in one month.

Kent farmers were also unhappy. They claimed the torrential rain was threatening to wreck the harvest as thousands of acres were battered flat by the wind and rain. Only a hot July, they said, could possibly rectify the damage.

The rain in June badly hit the second Test Match between England and Australia, threatened to ruin the Wimbledon fortnight, caused the Royal Pageant of the Horse at Windsor Great Park to be cancelled and forced the Glastonbury festival-goers to wallow in a sea of mud.

By the end of the month only the anorak and holiday trade were happy and coastal cinemas' managers said they had enjoyed one of the best-ever Junes.

Incredibly, the water companies said the June deluge had not lifted the threat of summer hosepipe bans. Some things never change! Dramatic thunderstorms in August, particularly on the night of the 12th/13th in West Kent, followed hot and sultry days.

Dry facts about the remarkable nineties

1991: After two hot summers, June 1991 brought disappointment. Temperatures failed to reach expected levels and in Dover it was the coolest June since 1916, with sea temperatures the lowest since records were first kept in 1957. In this disappointing summer the landlady at the Fox and Hounds, Toy's Hill — Kent's highest pub — kept a fire burning for her customers on midsummer's day. August brought thunderstorms to West Kent and a woman at Sevenoaks was killed by lightning as she hurried to shelter under a tree. It was another dry year; at Orpington the driest since 1976. The deficit of rainfall was 11.5 inches (294mm) over 1988-1991.

1992: January was the driest for at least 100 years and, at Sevenoaks, only half an inch (12.5mm) fell. The winter continued to remain dry with only 1.5 inches of rain at Sidcup, 24 per cent of the average. At Dover it was the driest February this century. In October there was heavy rain and thunderstorms with a lightning strike on a school near Wilmington, Dartford. There were spectacular sunsets during the autumn due to the eruption of Mount Pinutubo in the Phillipines.

1993: Another January without snow — the sixth in succession. In terms of unusual meteorological events this is one of the most remarkable of all and one without precedent. However, rime deposits found on January 3rd at Barnehurst following dense, freezing fog, were so thick that people were able to toboggan on them. Average pressure was the highest for the month of February for at least 34 years. March brought further drought and 28 days without rain was recorded at Sidcup.

1994: An area of low pressure crossed southern England on January 5th bringing rain but Kent avoided the heavy snow which affected other counties. The summer will be remembered for the long hot spell in mid-July which saw temperatures hit the upper eighties. It will also be noted for several thunderstorms which destroyed apple crops in East Peckham and Paddock Wood. The heatwave made July the fifth hottest this century but it was followed by more refreshing weather in August.

1995: A cold, wet start to the year with heavy rain in February. Summer got off to a blistering start with temperatures in May in the upper seventies and August was truly memorable — the warmest ever recorded. October was another warm, dry record-breaking month and, in places, November was the driest since 1956. There was snow and the accompanying chaos on the roads in early December followed by freezing rain on the penultimate day of the year which brought glaze to many parts of Kent.

1996: Below-average rainfall led to increased concerns about the possibility of hosepipe bans during the summer. Water companies in Kent said that underground reservoirs were critically low again. April was a dry month in many areas of Kent, sharp frosts were experienced in early May but June was sunny and warm with temperatures, away from the coast, exceeding 32C (90F). The sensational flash flood in Folkestone in August came in the middle of a series of torrential downpours throughout the county. Postling received 207.1mm (8ins) in August, 104mm of it on August 12th. This compares with 0.6mm measured the previous year from August 1st to the 30th. There were flurries of snow in some parts of Kent on Christmas Day.

1997: With another dry start to the year the media once again became obsessed with water stories and even John Gummer, Secretary of State for the Environment, spoke of the possibility of the Garden of England becoming fit only for growing maize and sunflowers in the next 50 years. Kent marked the fiftieth anniversary of the memorable winter of 1947, with the driest January since 1976. A dry April with its devastating frost on the 21st was followed, on May 6th by a hail, sleet and snow showers. June was exceptionally wet but July again lived up to the expectations raised for this month by the unusual succession of warm Julys in the 1990s.

There were violent thunderstorms on the night of August 12th and 13th with lightning flashing around midnight. A house was destroyed after being struck at Rochester and there were power cuts in the Maidstone area with 4,700 breaks in the grid circuit. At Dover it was the second warmest of any month — the warmest being August 1947.

1998: During the first week of January the wind reached 70 mph along the south coast and many ferries were cancelled. At Gillingham a boy was trapped beneath a fallen tree and the QE2 bridge at Dartford was closed. It was mild and virtually snowless through January to March but snow fell on the North Downs in mid April. On April 3rd a small tornado struck Wigmore, damaged a shed, tore up roof tiles and ripped branches from trees. As August began, towering thunderclouds built over Beckenham and gave 50 mm (two inches) — equivalent to a month's rainfall — in just an hour. It was also the wettest autumn since 1976 with totals approaching nearly 400mm at Dover. Three people were killed in thick fog near Ashford during the morning of December 16.

1999: The highest January temperature since the 1830s was recorded at Gravesend on January 6th with 16.3C (61.3F). It was more like early May. There were thunderstorms in late May with hailstones the

Car park Olympians: Canoeists at Canterbury find a place to practise in Sainsbury's flooded car park. October 2000.

(continued from previous page)

size of cherries but July was warm and very dry — the driest July on the Kent/Surrey border since 1825. The temperature reached 32.2C (90F) on August 1st in the Sevenoaks/Tonbridge area. Thousands of homes were without water. The Mid-Kent Water Company hired a plane to tow a banner reminding people that they needed licences for sprinklers. A small land devil, or fair-weather vortex caused damage at an antiques fair in Detling on July 31st. The temperature dropped by nearly three degrees on the morning of August 11th when southern parts of Kent experienced a 98 per cent solar eclipse.

At Gravesend, on September 11th, the temperature soared to 30C (86F), the highest value for that month since 1973. It was the warmest September overall since 1949. On October 24th the pressure fell to around 972 millibars and strong southerly winds reached 66mph at Dover. Several roads in east Kent were blocked by fallen trees. The Christmas period brought 70mph gusts and ships were storm-bound outside Dover harbour. There was flooding at Lamberhurst

Welcome 2000 — now Kent takes a battering

2000: A mild winter with no snow away from the Downs. April 4th was colder than most of the winter days with readings of 2.5C (37C) in the Tonbridge area and snow at Biggin Hill and Maidstone. It was the wettest April for more than 130 years at Dover. During the afternoon of May 8th enormous thunderclouds towered to great heights over the Weald. This brought the inevitable flash floods. The Eden was put on red alert by the Environment Agency and a rain gauge at Bough Beech Reservoir recorded 82.5mm (3.23inches) of rain in the space of one hour. The May rain total topped 200mm (7.85inches).

July was the coolest since 1988. Heavy rain fell after midnight on July 5th along the sandstone ridge in West Kent. The rain amounted to 65.3mm at Sevenoaks and accounted for 75 per cent of the month's rainfall total. September was also wet but warm and October provided extraordinary rainfall totals, almost four times the normal. Up to 180mm (seven inches) fell in the upper parts of the Medway, Beult, Rother and Teise in just three days, much of it in 12 hours. Sixteen severe flood warnings were issued for Kent and Sussex and extraordinary scenes in Yalding, East Peckham, Lamberhurst, Tonbridge and Maidstone made television news.. The most poignant moment for co-author of this book Ian Currie was to see, on national television, a boat rowed over the parking bay at Lamberhurst where a few weeks beforehand he had left his car. At that time Ian was in the village hall giving a talk on *"Epic Weather Events"*.

Waterlogged: Kent Messenger picture editor Barry Hollis captured this shot on Thursday October 12th of the countryside between Wateringbury and Tonbridge. Many acres of farmland were submerged.

Memories of '68: This was High Street, Tonbridge on Thursday October 12th. The water was still rising.

167

Floods 2000 — countdown to disaster

October 10th-13th:

CRACKED reservoirs, hosepipes bans, falling water levels belong to a previous century. Within 10 months of the start of a brand new millennium the people of Kent were dancing to a new tune and the performers could have been Wet, Wet, Wet!

No-one who lives in the riverside towns and villages will forget the month they know as "Ominous October". As seven inches of rain fell in the river valleys — mostly in 12 dramatic hours — urgent flood warnings turned into a horrific reality. Thousands of people were evacuated from homes in Yalding, Laddingford, East Peckham, Collier Street and Stilebridge and taken to the Cornwallis School at Linton.

The River Medway burst its banks at Maidstone and the borough council's emergency plan swung into action. At one time the river was running at a rate of 150 cubic metres per second (it is normally 12 cubic metres) and the Leigh barrier, near Tonbridge was lifted to control the volume of flood water. Here is the countdown to the disaster that followed:

Tuesday October 10th (9pm to 4am Wednesday): Torrential rain. As much as 50mm in places). Anxiety grows as weather forecasters warn of worsening weather ahead.

Wednesday October 11th (evening): Memories of September 1968 come flooding back as rain of almost tropical intensity falls on the south-east.

Thursday October 12th (dawn): Still raining. Levels reach 70 mm. River Teise bursts its banks and villagers at Lamberhurst are marooned in upstairs rooms as dirty brown floodwater closes A21 at both ends of village. Day off for pupils of Lamberhurst primary school.

Thursday October 12th (mid-day): Medway rising rapidly. Farmland begins to disappear. Environment Agency identifies 17 main areas of danger in Kent and Sussex.

Thursday October 12th (2pm): Leigh barrier (opened in mid-80s as a giant storage reservoir) swung into action. Controlled outflow helped to ease the danger of Tonbridge town being immediately engulfed as it was in 1968.

Thursday October 12th (4pm): First evacuations take place at Yalding, Laddingford and East Peckham. Firemen and members of 96 Squadron, 36 Engineer Regiment use inflatable boats to ferry people to safety. Police set up special emergency

centre at Sutton Road headquarters. Residents of Lyons Crescent, Vale Road and Lockside, Tonbridge advised to leave their homes. Tonbridge and Malling Council deploy staff in rotating shifts to help emergency services.

Thursday October 12th (6.30pm): River Beult bursts its banks. Raw sewage flows into Headcorn. Primary School and many homes are flooded. Parts of Smarden are also inundated. Old people and children from Tonbridge taken to Judd School in Brook Street. Sandbag distribution continues in all vulnerable areas. East Peckham bridge closes to traffic.

Leaving home: Kent Fire Brigade's rubber inflatables helps in the rescue operation at Yalding.

Thursday October 12th (from 7.30pm): Police advise remaining residents of Yalding to evacuate but many refuse. "I have lived in the village for 40 years", says landlord of the George pub, "and I've never known people to leave before. We're staying put".

Friday October 13th (dawn): Residents of The Square, Yalding see trees, garden furniture, pieces of wood floating through the village. "It's horrendous", says pensioner Rusty Morris. "I've never seen the water romp so fast. They've put ropes across the street to assist the firefighters".

Friday October 13th (9am): Scores of schools in Kent close including Laddingford, Headcorn, Collier Street, Kingswood, Yalding, Staplehurst, Tovil, Five Acre Wood, East Farleigh, Cornwallis Boughton Moncheslsea, Astor of Hever and all Maidstone schools. Maidstone braces itself for serious flooding. Motorists in Five Oak Green defy warnings and drive through village sending more waves into adjacent homes. Environment Agency says 4pm high tide will be the crucial hour. Police close town bridges.

Friday October 13th (mid-day): *Kentish Lady* passenger boat in danger of breaking moorings at Archbishop's Palace, Maidstone. Helicopter winches airman down to secure boat (see picture left). Army later called to attach stronger ropes. Register office

(at Archbishop's Palace) agrees to go ahead with six weddings planned for Saturday despite advice to call them off. Malta Inn, Allington closes. Police row to The Lees, Yalding to rescue black cat belonging to Mrs Mears.

Friday October 13th (4pm): Maidstone MP and Shadow Home Secretary, Ann Widdecombe visits Cornwallis School, Boughton Monchelsea where 65 evacuees are sheltering. "I found a real Dunkirk spirit", she said. "Everyone was pulling together". Kent Fire Brigade report receiving 400 calls during the emergency. At the height of the operation 30 fire engines and 150 personnel were deployed. At Tonbridge soldiers worked throughout the day to shore up the town's defences.

Friday October 13th (evening): Maidstone's multi-million pound Lockmeadow Leisure Centre closes. Emergency services put on a high state of alert as rivers continue to rise. Police spokeswoman Glenda Johnson says: "Floodwaters are not receding. We will advise people when it's safe to return home". Paramedics called to Cornwallis and Judd Schools to treat people suffering from hypothermia.

(continued on page 171)

Among the residents of Lamberhurst marooned in upstairs rooms waiting for the rescue services to arrive were
Claire de Garston said: We were badly affected by floods last Christmas but this is going to cost us thousands of poun
a height of four feet in the village centre. The monsoon conditions brought havoc to other Wealden villages. Skinners Garde
Fire crews were hard hit trying to cope with the rising flood waters in Sheephurst Lane area of Mard

New homes on Kentish flood plains blamed for frequency of flooding

WHO'S to blame for the severity of the Millennium Floods? Is it the hand of God, global warming or the decision by many local authorities in Kent to allow new homes to be built in flood plains — thereby reducing the amount of drainage facility for water?

These were the questions and possible answers which dominated television and radio news programmes in the wake of the worst flooding since 1968.

The Environment Agency said that it objects to 30,000 planning applications a year in areas prone to flooding but despite this 20 per cent of these are approved and many are in Kent. Although most are porches and conservatories and are regarded as trivial by local planners they still increase the area of building on a flood plain. Surplus water is forced back into the river unnaturally fast causing worse flooding downstream.

There is no doubt also that climate change is making Kent, with its 126 miles of coastline, rivers and valleys a "hot-spot" for flooding in which the risk to lives and property will increase tenfold over the next century.

The Environment Agency has said that while the north and west will see the greatest increase in rainfall, the south-east where most of the new development is taking place, is in the greatest danger of flooding.

In Kent those sudden intense thunderstorms are likely to continue and there will be a danger of flooding of low-lying land due to the rise in sea level.

This century the sea is expected to rise by 15-50cm as glaciers and snowfields melt. By 2050 the rise in level due to climate change will increase the frequency of dangerously high tides from once a century to once a decade. Kent will always be under threat.

The Met Office said it was impossible to confirm that the October floods were caused by man-made global warming but they were consistent with the centre's predictions of more extreme events.

(continued from page 169)

Saturday October 14th: Kent Messenger newspaper group publishes a Flood Special on the worst floods for a decade. Canoeists from Riverside Youth Centre enjoy a paddle in Sainsbury's car park, Canterbury. Floods reported at Sheppey particularly at Halfway where a foot of water laps doorsteps. National Trust advises anyone planning to visit properties in Kent to call first.

As reports of serious flooding come in from the Stockbury Valley, Whitstable, the Hoo Peninsula, Gillingham, Edenbridge, Brasted and many villages in the Sevenoaks area, the evacuees in their makeshift homes at Boughton Monchelsea and Tonbridge prepare to return to their flooded homes knowing that river levels remain dangerously high.

In Five Oak Green householders renew their call for better drainage systems in the village after they had been evacuated for the third time in 10 months.

Garston family at the Chequers public house. Landlady e've salvaged everything we could". The flood water rose to estate in Sissinghurst, was awash with raw sewage. otorists were stranded at Hawkenbury and Staplehurst.

Roads and railways grind to a halt as Millennium Storm batters Kent

THE low pressure which had hovered so disasterously above Kent and south-east England was all too soon followed by another even more ferocious brewing up again in the Atlantic. As the weekend of October 28/29th approached forecasters predicted gusts in excess of 70 mph and severe weather warnings were flashed across television screens. Kent braced itself for another battering. This had all the hallmarks of an "October '87".

In the village of Yalding, now known among locals as "the plughole of Kent", familes waited helplessly for the floods to return. At the Kent police headquarters in Maidstone a command unit prepared contingency plans. Senior figures from Kent Ambulance Brigade, the Fire Service, Coastguard, 36 Engineer Regiment and West Kent Health Authority alerted their teams. So did Kent County Council's emergency planning team, the Environment Agency, Southern Electric and Connex South East. Gold Control was ready.

The heaviest winds arrived on Sunday night with gusts in excess of 90mph and torrential rain cutting a swathe across the whole of southern England. By dawn more than 300 flood warnings were in force and emergency services were struggling to cope with thousands of fallen trees and stranded motorists.

In Kent power supplies were severed and there was havoc on the railways. Waves, 15 feet high battered the shore right round the coast. Unbelievably, six cross-Channel ferries carrying 6,000 passengers were stranded at sea for 20 hours because it was too dangerous for them to dock at Dover.

Kent and Sussex again bore the brunt. A twister struck Bognor Regis on Saturday. It returned the following day as a tornado, picking up 200 caravans in Selsey and hurling them around a park in a terrifying episode that was all over in minutes.

The Kent railway network — already suffering delays and cancellations because of the largest maintenance programme for a century — now experienced, on Monday October 30th, its worst day of disruption since January 1990. Trees, branches and leaves blocked the line. Commuter trains to London were cancelled. A Eurostar train driver bravely set off from Waterloo but took two hours to cover the 11 miles to Bromley where it was cancelled. All Channel shipping stopped. The QE2 bridge at Dartford closed.

On the roads hundreds of motorists abandoned their journeys and sometimes their vehicles as they ran into fallen trees and floodwater. Sections of the M25 were closed. Lorries bound for the Continent were stacked on the M20. The queue stretched back for many miles.

A widow in her 70s, already suffering from the second flooding in two weeks of her old farmhouse in New House Lane, Laddingford was saved from almost certain death by her smoke alarm which woke her at 2.15am on Tuesday October 31st. Mrs Bracher telephoned the fire brigade but remained inside the flooded and smoke-filled house with her caged birds.

After a tricky journey through the floods six fire engines arrived and Mrs Bracher was moved to safety in the flooded garage with her birds.

6,000 stranded at sea on Channel ferries

October 30th: As the P and O Stena ferry, the *Pride of Kent*, was pushed into dock at Dover on Monday morning because all attempts to tow her had failed, passengers questioned the company's decision to sail from Calais into the teeth of the worst storm for 13 years.

"It's down to the discretion of the master of each ship", said a P and O spokesman. "On this occasion six of them decided to sail".

A few miles out of Calais on Sunday night the ferries ran into waves that rose up around them like a gigantic wall. The winds were now in excess of 85mph and the passengers were about to experience the most terrifying night of their lives.

"After half an hour's sailing people began to panic", said Mr Douna Den from London. "Glasses were smashing. It was the worst trip of my life".

Robert Barnes from Upminster said people in the lounges were very ill. "The majority", he said, "just got drunk to pass the time".

"It was like a fairground", said Graham Munslow from Epsom. "People were being sick everywhere. When you walked into the coffee bar chairs were sliding to and fro because floors were slippery".

The first ferry finally docked at 11.30 am after 20 hours at sea followed by the other five. Most had sheltered in a natural bay off Deal as driving rain had forced the closure of Dover port.

Left: The River Medway north west of Paddock Wood looking towards Tonbridge.

21st century - the first five years

2001: After many places experienced their third wettest winter on record and following the previous record-breaking autumn rains, there were rockfalls and great instability of the cliffs in the Dover-Folkestone area.

Heavy hail caused much damage to cars, windows of houses and greenhouses on 26th June at South Darenth and Horton Kirby. The hail was preceded by temperatures as high as 86F (30C).

2002: February was the second mildest at Dover behind 1990 and 1866. Sevenoaks had a snowfree winter for the first time since 1974-5.

On 29th July the overnight temperature remained above 68F (20C) in the Bromley and Sidcup areas and then rose to 90F (32C). On the afternoon of 20th August, 41mm of rain fell at Beckenham and West Wickham causing much flooding.

A gale on 26th-27th October reached 70mph at Dover. Ferries were cancelled and 'Operation Stack' was initiated on the M20. Seven people were killed in the country as a result of high winds. November was very wet with 197mm (7.7ins) at Dover.

December was mild and wet. An observer at Sutton-at-Hone wrote of conditions after Christmas - "stinging nettles in full growth and fine condition, weeping willows retaining their summer foliage, a large and healthy caterpillar crawling across the road — more in danger of being run over than frost bite — bulbs shooting up, bumblebees and wasps everywhere and a resident frog still leaping around the garden!"

2003: A rare January snowfall on the 8th gave up to four inches around Farningham and day temperatures fell close to freezing but on the 27th East Malling recorded 63F (17.4C), the South-East's highest official January temperature. Snow returned on the 30th accompanied by gale-force northerly gusts. There was chaos on the motorways.

In April, Sevenoaks recorded a low of 19F (-7C) on both the 7th and 8th yet on the 16th measured 79F (26C). This was the highest mid-April temperature since 1949 in much of Kent. June was the warmest since 1976. In July, 91F (32.5C) was recorded at Tonbridge.

August brought record-breaking temperatures in excess of 100F (37.8C) F at Brogdale near Faversham and Gravesend, on the 10th. In Sevenoaks 90F (32C) was reached on seven consecutive days from 7th August.

There was a dramatic drop in temperature of some 10C on 22nd September as a cold front passed and that led to a tornado being reported at Bearsted. There were severe floods in Dover overnight on 27th and 28th September after 43.3mm (1.7ins) of rain fell. In November a gale blew down Chillenden Mill as winds reached 65mph.

2004: In what was generally a fairly mild January, an arctic cold front pushed south with a spell of heavy snow during the evening rush-hour on the 28th causing chaos on the roads. This was accompanied by vivid flashes of lightning, loud thunder and gale-force gusts of wind. The temperature plunged to several degrees below freezing with snow drifts three feet deep across rural lanes in the Wrotham area.

Many places had their warmest February day on the 4th. The mercury reached 62F (16.5C) at Sevenoaks and 64F (18C) at Gravesend. At night it did not fall below 52F (11C) at Gillingham, again a record. However, the last week was cold with some mostly light snow showers and a low of 17F (-8.5C) at Sevenoaks.

On 10th May there was a heavy thunderstorm in the Tenterden area with severe flooding. In July, a thunderstorm gave way to large hailstones in Dover, damaging 140 cars. There was flooding in Dover's streets.

On 9th August the night minimum remained above 71F (21.6C) in Sidcup and by day reached 89F (31.7C) at Edenbridge. Many places had no rain from 29th November to 14th December.

2005: This was the second successive February that reinforced the old adage "as the days grow longer the cold grows stronger". The first half of February was mild but from the 19th there was snow daily and the temperatures fell to almost 19F (-7C) at Tonbridge.

March began in wintry mode with heavy snow on the 2nd. Many schools were shut, the M2 was closed and there was chaos on Kent's roads. Bredhurst had 7.5ins (19cm) of level snow. No trains ran in the Ashford, Faversham and Dover areas. Bromley recorded 15 successive days of snow falling.

May saw the highest temperatures for the month since 1994, and 90F (31.8C) was measured at Wilmington. June was hot with the temperatures not falling below 70F (21C) at Langdon Bay. Wilmington reached 91F (32.7C).

On 10th September a violent thunderstorm hit West Kent and 50mm (2ins) of rain fell at Swanley, flooding the lower part of the town.

It was the second warmest October on record behind 2001. At Gravesend on the 30th the mercury reached 70F (21C).

Heavy snow fell over East Kent on 27th December with 7ins in Folkestone and 4ins at Rye.

People are standing on the ice in this remarkable scene of a frozen Herne Bay in the winter of 1963. This may never happen again.

Will pomegranates and bananas grow in Kent?

November 2002: Kent is known as the *Garden of England* due to its agricultural influence, extensive orchards and hop gardens. The delightful villages of the Weald of Kent boast some of the best cottage gardens in the country.

This image of Kent as a green and pleasant land is under threat because of climate change. In place of the delphiniums and the lupins and the perfect lawn, the county could be growing citrus fruits, pomegranates or even bananas.

This month, the National Trust and the Royal Horticultural Society, along with experts from the UK Climate Impacts Programme, launched the world's first definitive study on the problem of climate change.

Many of the local plant collections in the care of the National Trust in places such as Sissinghurst, Knole, Emmetts will have to be moved hundreds of miles if they are to survive and existing gardens redesigned with different plants.

The average temperature in Kent is set to rise by 2-5C (at least 4F) in the summer and 2-3C in the winter in the next 50 years. Snow will become a distant memory and frost a rarity.

Richard Bisgrove of Reading University, joint author of *Gardening in the Global Greenhouse* says that Francis Bacon's comments about England — "it's very pleasant to sit outside but not pleasant enough to sit still" — would no longer be true.

1953 flood repeat may kill hundreds

31 January 2003: If there were to be a repeat of the storm surge which hit Kent, Essex and East Anglia 50 years ago, more than two thirds of the coastal defences would fail and hundreds of people would die, according to a new report.

On the 50th anniversary of the 1953 floods when 307 people perished and more than 1,000 miles of coastline was breached, a London University research centre says today's storm barriers would not be able to cope.

Scientist, David Crichton says more lives will be lost because of the increased number of people living and working in the danger zone and the absence of a large standing army to assist with rescue work.

Metro Bus 404 on the 161 route battling through the snow at Chislehurst on the morning of 8th January 2003 — the heaviest January fall for 12 years. Picture by John King.

January white-out at Bluewater

8th January: Britain's biggest shopping centre, Bluewater, between Dartford and Gravesend, shut today for the first time since it opened in 1999, as London and parts of Kent experienced its heaviest snowfall for 12 years.

Eighty schools in Kent also closed, including every one in the Dartford and Gravesham boroughs. Kent County Council declared a snow and ice emergency and warned that roads would turn into an "ice rink".

Snow in the centre of London, usually the last place it settles, was measured at 2½ inches (5cm).

A spokesperson for Bluewater, who said she had taken two hours to drive her normal 10 minute journey, said the decision to close the massive centre was taken "because we cannot guarantee the safety of the people entering the site".

The M20, M25 and A20 were all badly affected and the AA Roadwatch described the roads as treacherous. At one point there was a 25-mile tailback on the M25. Nearly all train operators reported problems; the Dockland Light Railway was closed for three hours.

In London thousands of commuters were forced to stay in hotels and passengers camped in airports when their flights were cancelled.

An icy flurry in January 2003 took everyone by surprise but did not deter one of our authors, who enjoyed his usual early-morning dip in the unheated swimming pool, nearly 700 feet above sea level, near Westerham.

GRAVESEND REPORTER

GRAVESEND'S BEST-SELLING NEWSPAPER SINCE 1856   THURSDAY 14th AUGUST, 2003   **35p**

100.6°F

Bookies take a beating on hottest day ever recorded

BOOKIES have been forced to pay out a massive £500,000 after temperatures soared past the magic 100ºF mark in Gravesend last weekend, setting a new record for Britain's hottest ever day.

But now they claim gambling fanatics have also been rushing out to put bets on the coming winter being the coldest since records began.

● For full story see page 3

Kent once again holds the record for the hottest day ever known. On Sunday 10th August the temperature at both Brogdale near Faversham and Gravesend soared past 100F — the first time anywhere in Britain that the thermometer has officially exceeded the century mark.

Brogdale, the home of the National Fruit Collection, also boasts a weather station and the high of 101.3F (38.5C) easily beat the previous highest value in the country. Just along the coast the Port of London Weather Station at Gravesend recorded 100.6F (38.1C).

The previous highest England recorded temperature was 99F (37.1C) at Cheltenham (Gloucestershire) on 3rd August 1990 and before that 98F (37C) at Canterbury, and Epsom in Surrey, in August 1911. For some time Gravesend thought they had the record but Brogdale finally took the prize. Sean Clarke of the Met Office said that Gravesend benefited from the heat generated by London.

"But more important", he said, "it has sandy soil which warms quickly. It's a bit like walking across hot sand in bare feet."

101.3F Gravesend pipped by Brogdale home of the fruit collection

METEOROLOGISTS who work for the Port of London Weather Station at Ebbsfleet, Gravesend spent seven weeks believing they had the record for the hottest day ever in the UK.

The high of 100.1F (38.1C) recorded on 10th August 2003 was acknowledged immediately, to the delight of the meteorological fraternity on Thameside.

"It's like winning an Olympic medal and setting a world record", said one of them. "A remarkable achievement".

As the mayor sent his congratulations and stories appeared in national newspapers, questioning the validity of the record going to an esturial town, it emerged that the hottest place in Britain was actually a few miles away from the town given the accolade.

Brogdale, Faversham had recorded a reading of 101.3F (38.5C) . The Met Office said the new record

The famous instrument enclosure at Brogdale, Faversham which recorded the new record high on 10th August 2003.

was announced seven weeks later because results from Brogdale were only checked monthly.

A spokeswoman said: "Gravesend is a real time observation station, so we get their results every day, hence that is why we could announce it was the hottest place. In Faversham, the results come in every month.

"We had to go and verify the information at Faversham to check the equipment and check it was running correctly. That weather station is not run by the Met Office but by a volunteer so we had to check it ourselves and release the result now."

In a remarkable coincidence, Ian Currie was due to give a talk in Faversham on the afternoon of the announcement of the new record. "I arrived early", he said, "and went in search of Britain's hottest weather station. I found it in the home of the National Fruit Collection at Brogdale and took a picture of the famous instrument.

Ian also met the lady in charge of the station, Mary Pennell, who said that Brogdale is situated on the dip slope of the North Downs and on this record-breaking day the air of the lee side was subsiding and warming in the gentle south-south east winds.

The exceptionally hot weather prompted a rush on barbecue gear, salads, beer and soft drinks. Supermarkets in Kent said they had brought in more meat, fruit juices and bottled water to meet demand. Tesco reported they had sold 150,000 litres of sun cream and Asda two million tubs of ice cream.

The only really unhappy people were the bookmakers who lost more than £300,000 to punters who had backed the record-breaking temperatures, according to Ladbroke's spokesman, Warren Lush.

Bewl Water, Lamberhurst — the largest reservoir in the south-east — eventually dropped to the lowest level ever known. Picture by Southern Water. See story next page.

Brothers Ben and Joe Crellin, from Northumberland are amazed by the expanse of hard mud - baked earth in South-East England's largest reservoir at Bewl, near Lamberhurst. Reservoirs in Northumberland have not been known to dry up.

Bewl Water bailed out by the Medway

ONE of the longest spells of dry weather in Kent — certainly since the "desert year of 1921" — began in November 2004 and lasted until the end of 2006, which was the hottest year since records began.

During that time forests blazed, rivers, lakes and reservoirs shrunk to their lowest-ever levels and weather records were frequently broken. Every few months or so experts claimed that change to our climate was unstoppable and greenhouse gases in the atmosphere were to blame.

In May 2004, several weeks before the dry spell began, scientists at the Natural Environment Reserarch Council claimed the new source of atmospheric pollution could mean thousands of Britons having to wear charcoal masks and stay indoors during heatwaves to avoid clouds of ozone.

With Kentish heatwaves — and temperatures in excess of 100F— expected to become more regular, report after report revealed previously unknown details of the dangers facing children, animals, the elderly and the asthmatic.

The Environment Agency released figures in June 2004 showing that Southern Britain faced a serious water shortage; this densely populated region, they claimed, has less water per head than the desert states of Syria and the Sudan.

They were proved to be right. After the dry winter of 2004-5 Southern Water applied to the Agency for emergency powers to help refill Bewl Water at Lamberhurst, which had dropped to the lowest level ever known. The permit was granted and 20 million litres of water from the River Medway was used to top up Kent, and southern England,'s largest reservoir.

As the water shortage became even more acute a correspondent to a Kent newspaper asked why water could not be moved a few hundred miles from damp Scotland to his overcrowded county. Another letter writer blamed the shortage on Deputy Prime Minister John Prescott's continuing persuance of house building when the county's natural resources were so dangerously overconsumed.

In reply to the first question the Environment Agency said water is heavy and requires great energy to pump it over long distances. The scheme would almost certainly be blocked on the grounds of cost. Of the second question there was no reply but the people of Ashford and the Thames Gateway knew that Prescott's new homes would be concentrated in vast new local conurbations.

The River Medway water diversion was followed by the inevitable hosepipe bans right across Kent. By February 2006 most homes in Kent were forbidden to use hosepipes or sprinklers. Southern Water and Mid Kent went further; they applied for drought orders to ban all non-essential use, including the watering of sports fields. Thames Water followed.

Trees collapse under weight of April snow

2006: February began with temperatures below freezing both day and night but no frost was visible and the ground remained soft in places such as Edenbridge Westerham. By the end of February, after two successive drier than average winters, Bewl Water, Lamberhurst was at record low level.

April is renowned for its fickle weather and overnight on the 9th and 10th heavy snow fell in parts of West Kent. In Tunbridge Wells 6ins (15cm) of snow caused trees to collapse onto railway lines. On 13th June a thunderstorm flooded the Dartford Tunnel. July was the warmest month of all time — a national record. At Edenbridge and Gillingham temperatures reached 95F (35C) on the 19th and in the latter 17 days exceeded 80F (26.7C).

September was the warmest ever nationally and 84F (29C) was recorded as late as the 21st at Herne Bay. October was the third warmest month ever and the autumn, as a whole, the warmest on record.

An outstanding year.

Meet the weather birds

On the left, Kaddy Lee-Preston, BBC TV South East's girl with the golden hair (and smile) and the comely Gemma Humphries, who presents the regional weather for Meridian TV. Both girls trained as meteorologists with the Met Office before moving on to become TV forecasters. In 2007, Kaddy won The Royal Television Society Best Regional Personality Award.

2006 the hottest year ever

THE almost unprecedented series of record temperatures in Kent throughout 2006 saw more hosepipe bans, more woodland fires, more people preferring Margate to Mauritius and more gardeners giving up their attempts to keep lawns green.

In July, the hottest month ever known, garden centres and DIY stores ran out of water butts and many Kentish towns abandoned their traditional floral displays and hanging baskets.

The hosepipe bans were introduced in May and, ironically, co-incided with the wettest May for 26 years. June was drier and warmer and July was truly memorable. Over the entire country the month saw a mean average temperature of 67F (19.7C). The hottest day was 19th July with 95F (35C).

The first Kent water company to ban the use of hosepipes was Dover and Folkestone, followed by Thames Water, Southern Water and Mid Kent Water. Those who defied the restrictions were threatened with a fine of £1,000. Most water companies said they might have to introduce standpipes but this did not prove necessary.

The summer's heatwave had unusual casualties. Among those unable to find enough food to survive and taken to wildlife rescue centres in Kent were young badgers, foxes, deer, hedgehogs and birds of prey. The July sun had baked the ground so hard that worms and other invertebrates had either died or dug too deep.

Insect numbers also went into decline due to the lack of moisture. Even the tiniest bat, the pipistrelle, found they were unable to consume their usual quota of 3,000 insects a night. Many simply starved to death.

The records tumbled again in the warmest September ever known.

On the last day of December, 2006 was declared the hottest year since records began in 1659.

The earthquake they were waiting for

AN earthquake, measuring 4.3 on the Richter scale hit the east coast of Kent in the early hours of Saturday 28th April, 2007. The 'quake was the largest in Britain since 2002 when a tremor measuring 5.0 hit Dudley in the West Midlands. Dr Roger Musson, a seismologist at the British Geological Survey said: "There was no short term warning of this earthquake, but we have been expecting one in the Straits of Dover for the last 25 years".

The force of the tremor was felt in Hythe, Romney Marsh, Dover and Deal but it was the Foord valley area of Folkestone which was the hardest hit. Scores of homes were damaged but, miraculously, only one person, a woman in her thirties, was injured.

More than 800 calls were made to Shepway District Council's emergency response centre following the 'quake. Kent Fire and Rescue received a further 200 calls from people worried about gas leaks and falling debris.

More than 40 homes were classed as too dangerous to live in. Families were housed in temporary accommodation including the Salvation Army Centre in Canterbury Road, Folkestone.

To the relief of foreign travellers, Channel Tunnel services were unaffected as the tunnel was built to

A chimney pot totters on a roof in Folkestone.

endure tremors stronger than the one which hit the area.

Terrified residents, unaware of the earthquake, thought a terrorist attack was under way. Michael Howard, the former Conservative leader and MP for Folkestone and Hythe said: "I was having breakfast at the time and I felt the earth move. A tree fell in our garden and a picture fell off the wall. Our electricity went off".

While earthquakes are a relatively rare phenomenon in Kent, the county has suffered a number of minor 'quakes. The largest was in 1382 when the Bell Tower of Canterbury Cathedral was severely damaged and six bells 'shook down'.

The summer of 2007 - forget it!

KENT did not suffer from the acute floods affecting much of the heart of England during the summer of 2007 but the county was battered by torrential rain in both June and July, and late August. Mid-summer was one of the wettest ever — in stark contrast to the long, hot, drought-ridden weeks of 2006.

June was one of the wettest months on record in Britain. Average rainfall across the country was 140 millimetres (5.5 inches), more than double the June average. July had unsettled weather and above-average rainfall throughout the month, peaking on 20th July as an active frontal system dumped more than 120mm (4.7 inches) of rain on the West Midlands.

The year began with a brief wintry spell in Kent. A gale on 18th January led to the deaths of 19 people nationally, as a deep area of low pressure moved across northern England. The QE2 bridge at Dartford closed, cross-Channel ferries were suspended and 'Operation Stack' saw miles of stationary lorries on the M20. On the whole it was Kent's mildest January since 1921 and many places experienced the warmest winter on record, with March producing the lowest temperatures.

April was also the warmest ever known with several areas enjoying the rare phenomenon of a completely dry month. It was the sunniest April too, with 276 hours of sunshine at Edenbridge. Garden flowers bloomed early and abundantly.

Kent prepared itself for another dry, hot summer but it was not to be. The rains returned in May, with 38.6mm (1.5 ins) in Maidstone on the 28th. Torrential rain became a feature of the next two months with Minster (Sheppey) suffering flash floods and power cuts in early July. On Tuesday, 3rd July, for only the fifth time in 23 years of summer seasons, the open air performance (of Noel Coward's *Hay Fever*) at Hever castle was cancelled; the combination of rain and heavy lightning was considered too dangerous to the audience.

On 21st August, after days of damp, cloudy misery, 50mm (2ins), a month's average rainfall, fell in four hours, causing flash floods in Tankerton, Faversham, Hythe, Hawkinge and Whitstable. Householders were left with a big clear up job.

Although the August bank holiday weekend brought some sunshine, the summer of 2007 will be memorable only for the misery of flooding throughout the kingdom.

Index to Names of Towns, Villages and Rivers

The Authors

BOB OGLEY

Bob was born in Sevenoaks, has lived all his life in the county and is proud to be a Kentish Man. An author of more than a dozen books he has travelled extensively in pursuit of information and has discovered an unexpected supplementary career as a speaker to organisations. He is also a regular broadcaster on BBC Radio Kent.

Bob is a former editor of the Sevenoaks Chronicle and author of *In The Wake of The Hurricane* — the book on the great storm of 1987 which went into the top ten bestseller lists and stayed there for seven successive months. He has also written *Kent at War, Biggin on The Bump and Doodlebugs and Rockets.* His latest is a history on Kent in the 19th century, following the popular four volume series on Kent in the 20th century. The books he has published with his wife, Fern, have raised more than £101,000 for various charities.

MARK DAVISON

Mark has always shown a keen interest in the weather. As a child he could not be persuaded to come indoors out of the snow. When, as a teenager, the great storm hit Hook in 1973 he was reprimanded by his parents for going off in search of news stories rather than helping them mop up their flooded home.

After leaving school in Kingston, he joined the Kingston Borough News just in time to cover the 1976 drought stories. Later he joined the Surrey Mirror Series and is now deputy editor at Reigate, the town where he lives.

For a number of years Mark has compiled a local history page in his newspaper which is still a popular feature today. He has written a series of photographic 'Remembered' books about Surbiton and the surrounding areas.

IAN CURRIE

Ian has always been fascinated by the ever changing moods and patterns of our skies.

The spectacular thunderstorm of September 1958 and the prolonged deep winter snows of 1962-63 were childhood memories that have never faded.

Sharing his interest with others has been a feature of Ian's life. He writes a weekly weather column for a number of Surrey newspapers and is now a full-time freelance weatherman, author and speaker. Ian is the BBC Southern Counties Weather Watch presenter

A graduate of Geography and Earth Science, he regularly talks to local groups and societies.

He is a Member of the Climatological Observers Link and is a Fellow of the Royal Meteorological Society; he publishes a quarterly magazine *Weather Eye.*

Books available from Froglets Publications, Brasted Chart, Westerham, Kent TN16 1LY Tel: 01959 562972 Fax: 01959 565365

OTHER COUNTY WEATHER BOOKS
By Bob Ogley, Ian Currie and Mark Davison

The Essex Weather Book
ISBN 9781872337319..............................£10.99

The Sussex Weather Book
ISBN 9781872337135 (Temp OP).............£10.99

The Hampshire and Isle of Wight Weather Book
ISBN 9781872337203.............................£9.95

The Berkshire Weather Book
ISBN 9781872337487..............................£9.95

HURRICANE SERIES

In The Wake of The Hurricane National Edition by Bob Ogley
ISBN 9781872337616.............................£10.99

Surrey In The Hurricane
by Mark Davison and Ian Currie
ISBN 9780951301920..............................£8.95

Eye on The Hurricane in the Eastern Counties
by Bob Ogley and Kev Reynolds
Paperback ISBN 9780951301968.............£7.95
Hardback ISBN 9780951301975............£11.95

London's Hurricane
by Mark Davison and Ian Currie
Paperback ISBN 9780951301937.............£7.95
Hardback ISBN 9780951301982.............£11.95

WAR AND AVIATION SERIES

Biggin On The Bump
The most famous fighter station in the world
by Bob Ogley
Paperback ISBN 9781872337050............£10.99
Hardback ISBN 9781872337104 (Temp OP) £16.99

Ghosts of Biggin Hill by Bob Ogley
Paperback ISBN 9781872337418.............£12.99
Hardback ISBN 9781872337463..............£16.99

Doodlebugs and Rockets by Bob Ogley
Paperback ISBN 9781872337210............£12.99
Hardback ISBN 9781872337227............£16.95

Kent at War (1939-1945) by Bob Ogley
Paperback ISBN 9781872337821............£12.99
Hardback ISBN 9781872337494............£16.99

Surrey at War (1939-1945) by Bob Ogley
Paperback ISBN 9781872337654............£12.99
Hardback ISBN 9781872337708..(OP)..£16.99

Westerham and Crockham Hill in the War
by Helen Long
ISBN 9781872337401...............................£8.95

OTHER LOCAL HISTORY BOOKS

Underriver: Samuel Palmer's Golden Valley
By Griselda Barton and Michael Tong
ISBN 9781872337456...............................£9.95

Tales of Old Tunbridge Wells by Frank Chapman
ISBN 9781872337258....**Special Offer**.....£8.95

Sevenoaks Chronicle of the Century
by Bob Ogley and Roger Perkins
ISBN 9781872337265.............................£14.95

CHRONICLE SERIES

Kent - A Chronicle of the Century
by Bob Ogley

Volume One 1900-1924
Hardback ISBN 9781872337241.............£16.99
Paperback ISBN 9781872337197............£12.99

Volume Two 1925-1949
Hardback ISBN 9781872337845.............£17.99
Paperback ISBN 9781872337890............£12.99

Volume Three 1950-1974
Hardback ISBN 9781872337166.............£17.99
Paperback ISBN 9781872337111............£12.99

Volume Four 1975-1999
Hardback ISBN 9781872337067.............£16.99
Paperback ISBN 9781872337012............£12.99

Boxed Set Hardback 9781872337159.....£68.00
Boxed set Paperback 9781872337753....£50.00

Kent 1800-1899 by Bob Ogley
Hardback ISBN 9781872337517.............£18.99
Paperback ISBN 9781872337562...........£14.99

e-mail: bobogley@frogletspublications.co.uk
www.frogletspublications.co.uk